SMOKE
SCREENING

Title: Smoke Screening
Copyright © 2019 by Jim Damron

Printed in the United States of America
ISBN 978-1-946425-41-6

Book Design by CSinclaire Write-Design
Book Cover by 99 Designs

• WRITE WAY •
PUBLISHING COMPANY
RALEIGH, NORTH CAROLINA
www.writewaypublishingcompany.com

SMOKE
SCREENING

Narratives to Navigate
Caregiver Burnout

Jim Damron

• WRITE WAY •
PUBLISHING COMPANY
RALEIGH, NORTH CAROLINA

CONTENTS

ACKNOWLEDGMENT

THIS SECTION OFTEN COMPRISES a list of people who assisted authors in completing their books. The section continues page after page recognizing each and every person who contributed to the author's finished product, and deservedly so. Writing a book is rarely solely an individual accomplishment. I too could list several people who helped in various ways, but I will mention only one.

Charlotte Hamlin, PhD devoted a considerable amount of time to this endeavor of mine. Her expertise in storytelling and narrative construction was invaluable. Charlotte helped shape a mediocre manuscript of experiences into a polished collection of stories. If the book was a movie, I may have written the screenplay but Charlotte provided insight with the wardrobe, makeup, score, and lighting. She was integral in bringing these experiences to life.

With each passing chapter, Charlotte provided encouragement, direction, and feedback. Knowledgeable people listen to advice. Wise people apply that advice constructively. Comparing the first draft with the final one proves that, in this instance, I was wise. I am incredibly grateful for Charlotte's encouragement and guidance as I embarked on this new writing adventure.

INTRODUCTION

WORKING IN HEALTHCARE IS both rewarding and challenging. Caregivers have the privilege of participating in restoring health to people. Witnessing someone recover from illness is both gratifying and satisfying. However, the fast-paced healthcare environment provides little time to cope with difficult situations. The higher demand for productivity combined with the declining availability of resources lends itself to increased stress, frustration, and burnout in this industry.

I know. I've burned out.

Medical professionals experience a higher rate of burnout than most other professionals.[1] Because of its increasing prevalence, burnout has some saying it's more a question of *when* rather than *if* it will occur. I disagree. I do not believe burnout is inevitable. But despite our efforts, there are times when burnout occurs. In that case, having tools at your disposal to mitigate, lessen, and work through the symptoms is invaluable.

---

[1]   Lotte N. Dyrbye, et al. Burnout Among Health Care Professionals: A Call to Explore and Address This Underrecognized Threat to Safe, High-Quality Care, *National Academy of Medicine,* July 5, 2017. pp. 1-11.

1

When it comes to burnout, there is no shortage of remedies. But remedies are individual dependent. Each person is unique, and what may work for one may not work for another. That said,

twenty years in medicine has taught me
the most effective tools to manage burnout.

TALE OF TRUTH AND STORY

Two women named Truth and Story lived on the outskirts of a village. Each one believed she was the prettiest, and they argued incessantly. One day they decided to have a contest to settle the matter. Each woman would walk through the village and whoever attracted the most attention from the villagers would be considered the prettiest.

The next day, they walked to the edge of the village. Truth decided to go first. She was certain she would win because everyone seeks and cherishes Truth. With her plain clothes, Truth walked through the village and greeted everyone she saw. She smiled and invited others to join her along her journey. To her surprise, most people hesitated and declined her invitation. Some dismissed her altogether. Fearing she would lose the contest, Truth decided the best way to attract as much attention as possible would be to disrobe and walk back through the village wearing nothing at all. This time the villagers not only refused to talk with her but they also fled and ran into their houses, shutting and locking their doors. Hanging her head in shame, Truth told Story it was her turn.

Story walked into the village and immediately people came out of their homes and greeted her as she passed.

Villagers commented on her garments saying things like, "I love your dress." "Where did you get those shoes?" "My mother had a hat just like that." As Story talked, the villagers smiled, listened, and followed her to the edge of the village. By the time Story arrived back to Truth, practically the entire village had come out into the streets.

Truth was defeated and confused. "Why do people shun me and flock to you?" she asked. "Do people no longer value Truth?"

"Ah," sighed Story. "People do value Truth, but they do not like plain Truth and often flee from naked truth. If you want people to accept you, you must clothe yourself in the right attire." Story then dressed Truth in her clothes and Truth walked back through the village. People clung to her every word to hear the wisdom she had to give.

This folktale is a great reminder that

Truth is nearly always best heard when dressed by Story.

REASONS FOR THIS BOOK

First, stories move people. When we desire to learn, grow, and understand more about ourselves, we reach for stories.[2] Narratives have a way of helping us reflect on the important things in life and discover the deeper meanings underneath them. It is in these deep reflections that life transformation happens.

---

[2]   Rita Charon, *Narrative Medicine: Honoring the Stories of Illness* (New York, Oxford University Press, 2006), vii.

Second, stories help explain situations that are difficult to communicate. They are a great way for people to express themselves. Stories evoke emotions and can produce oxytocin in our bodies, which is beneficial for motivation and for limiting depression. Thus, stories provide an informational and therapeutic benefit for handling burnout.

It's for these reasons that I wrote this book.

Structure of the Book

Throughout this book, I serve as the narrator. Almost all the reflections and thoughts are in first person. Occasionally, I refer to myself in the third person when the dialogue or the situation warrants.

The title of each chapter corresponds to a movie whose name reflects the narrative of the events. The movie titles are not necessarily my favorite movies. I chose these particular relevant movies because some of the best stories are found in film and, frankly, we all love movies.[3]

Each story reflects the events as I personally experienced them during my professional career as a Respiratory Therapist with one exception. In Chapter 10, "Keeping the Faith," the actual dialogue and specific situation are fictitious. However, all of the events of the story are based on actual cases I personally experienced or was intimately familiar with, even the ending. For brevity, I combined all the cases into one situation that I felt best galvanized the underlying narrative.

---

[3] The film industry generates billions of dollars every year (over $43 billion in 2017), https://deadline.com/tag/ibisworld/

To protect anonymity and to maintain the movie theme, the names of the people were changed to reflect the main characters in each chapter's corresponding film. Some quotes are not exact due to a lack of clear memory, but I maintained the quotes to continue the narrative style. Also, some characters (for example, Dr. Wolfson in *Flatliners—Revisited*) are an amalgam of more than one person.

At the end of each chapter, there are two sections: 1) a section titled *Reel to Real* where I apply the theme of the movie to the events in the story and 2) a section titled *Smoke Screen Test* where I ask self-assessment questions to help the reader identify areas of their life where they may be vulnerable to burnout. The questions and the "tools" highlight specific life lessons I have learned and practiced as a person and a professional to navigate burnout. I hope you can relate to the stories and answer the questions so that you can better recognize and manage burnout in your life.

CHAPTER 1

ANGER MANAGEMENT

ONE OF MY FONDEST memories is sitting in a movie theater with my father watching the film *The Naked Gun*. With each pun and piece of satirical dialogue, the room collectively howled with uncontrollable fits of laughter. There were no worries or concerns, only strangers expressing their enjoyment.

An overweight gentleman in front of me giggled throughout the entire film causing the whole row to vibrate. To my right, a couple fell into each other's lap when laughter removed their ability to sit upright. One lady squawked like a duck while another chuckled with machine-gun staccato. Happiness enveloped the room because laughter soothes the soul.

I often tried to bring this medicinal experience to my patients because, as the saying goes, laughter is the best medicine. Laughing decreases stress and protects against caregiving burnout. Though the treatment usually works, it also can be dangerous—as I found out!

DAVE'S COTTON WALL

I first met Dave in a sub-acute care facility where I worked immediately after graduating from Respiratory Therapy school. Respiratory was my third career, coming after science presenter and dive instructor. I earned my Scuba Instructor license after completing undergraduate studies. During my two-year tenure as an instructor, I taught people with varying vocational backgrounds. Many students worked in medicine. Because I was considering a career change, several students suggested I explore the pulmonary field. Two years later I was a licensed practitioner.

Dave was one of my first patients. I'll never forget him. From the moment he entered the nursing facility, Dave hid his face. Like a child afraid of ghosts, Dave pulled his sheet and blanket over his head as a refuge from people's stares. He permitted no one behind this cotton wall. He refused therapy, medicine, and practically any interaction with staff.

Dave was a young African American gentleman, too young for an end-stage cancer diagnosis (as if there is an age old enough to have such news). Just a few months prior, physicians told Dave the grim prognosis. There was nothing else to do. Cancer had won, medicine had lost. The war was a short one, and Dave had come out of the battlefield with more scars than he had brought in.

Just shy of his thirtieth birthday, Dave received the news that he had esophageal cancer. Despite medical advances, a cancer diagnosis continued to be synonymous with a death sentence. Dave did not accept this prognosis.

Dave was single with no immediate family. He had been living on his own since he became an adult. He had no siblings, and his parents had passed away several years ago. Dave wanted a family of his own, especially a wife. The cancer diagnosis made that dream problematic. Dave wanted to fight this battle with cancer and win an opportunity to fulfill his dream. Physicians obliged.

A month before coming to the nursing home, Dave walked into the hospital for his first round of radiation therapy. He entered the treatment room wearing only a gown and lay on the frigid table. A large machine circled overhead. Dave remained motionless as the machine screeched into operation. Beams of rays exited the machine and traveled through his neck, leaving scattered bits of radiation in their wake. Dave remained calm throughout the procedure until an ominous smell reached his nose. The odor of burning flesh was unmistakable. Physicians warned Dave of this effect, but nothing could have prepared him. Dave questioned the sanity of permitting someone to burn his body to beat cancer. At the time, that was the recommended therapy. Unfortunately, the radiation did not destroy the cancer. It only made it angry.

Dave's esophageal cancer proliferated and metastasized everywhere, and the cancer boasted its victory by leaving an indelible mark on Dave's face. The effect of radiation therapy caused Dave's upper lip to swell to four times its original size. It was so large it occluded both his nares. As a result, physicians had to create another opening for Dave to breathe. Surgeons placed a tracheostomy tube in Dave's neck to ensure he maintained a patent (open) airway.

Radiation also discolored Dave's skin and made it raw. Dry flakes of flesh fell from his neck continuously like a snake shedding its skin. Sores developed around the circumference of his neck, and bleeding occurred daily. Dave's disfigurement made him self-conscious and unwilling to display his defect. As a result,

Dave protected himself from potential stares and comments by hiding behind his bed linen.

Dave was miserable and angry. Cancer robbed him of his future and left him with pain and suffering. Dave recoiled at the thought of someone suctioning his airway. A soft touch to his neck felt like a knife stab. A small breeze equaled a slap to a freshly sunburned back. This reality sent Dave into a downward spiral of despair and self-loathing. He wallowed in self-pity and depression. He hated his situation. Who could blame him? *How would I respond if I were suddenly given a terminal prognosis of one year? And to have it shortened by six months after a medical intervention, I can't imagine!*

Dave's rage persisted but having a room to himself assuaged his resentment. Dave relished the solace and solitude. He was used to being alone, and he wanted it to stay that way. Dave would again be disappointed.

CANCER BUDDY

About two weeks after Dave came to the facility, I watched medical transporters bring Buddy into Dave's room on a mobile gurney. He was Caucasian and significantly older than Dave, evidenced by the gray-haired crown of splendor that adorned his head. Buddy also had gray stubble on his face and a permanent scowl on his forehead. He exuded toughness and disdain. Buddy was a former police officer. He had seen the worst of society and bore that disgust in his mannerisms and attitude. He responded to all inquiries about his history and health with yelling. At least, that is what we assumed. Buddy had a laryngectomy, a complete removal of his larynx or voice box. In his case, cancer had chosen his throat as a base of operation. The only way Buddy could vocalize was through the assistance of an electronic speech aid that provided the artificial vibrations necessary to make sounds. This intervention allowed him to phonate but not normally.

To communicate, Buddy grabbed his electronic device and held it to his throat. He mouthed the words he wished to say as the device vibrated. As he spoke, Buddy violently waved his free arm and pointed while electric shaver-like tones emanated from his throat. The sounds resembled that of a drowning robot.

Over the next several days, Buddy shared his story. Buddy was a crime fighter. He had joined the police force at a young age. His plan was to retire from law enforcement with a good pension and live the rest of his life with his children and grandchildren. "But this #@*!! cancer made me retire early!" Buddy explained. Cancer had waged war against Buddy too. Like Dave, he survived, but at a high price.

A TALE OF TWO AIRWAYS

A plastic artificial airway protruded from Dave's neck. The tracheostomy tube provided access for cleaning. Caring for Dave's airway should have been straightforward, but Dave reacted to the process violently. Whenever I touched Dave's neck with a dampened Q-tip, Dave recoiled furiously. "Sorry, Dave," I repeatedly said throughout each cleaning, "just another minute and I will be done." When I inserted the catheter to clean Dave's tracheostomy tube, he gagged violently. Each drop of saline on his skin caused painful retractions. Any dressing change induced panic and fear of the anticipated agony. When I finished, I always apologized one last time. Dave accepted the apology by rolling onto his side and shedding a tear that was partly from pain and partly from relief.

There is a particular emotion that surfaces when pain is inevitable—a mixture of trepidation and anguish. Because of the frequency of the tracheostomy care intervention, Dave developed a Pavlovian-type response to me. I represented misery. Eventually, the mere announcement that tracheostomy care was coming brought tears to Dave's eyes.

Buddy's response differed. With each cleaning, I took out my airway kit and removed the Q-tips, dressing, and saline. I wiped the area around Buddy's stoma, the opening in his neck. Surrounding the opening was no artificial airway, just a cesspool of mucous. Like an abandoned swimming pool, his stoma attracted residue that required removal. I dampened a piece of gauze and cleaned the area using several passes. Like Dave, Buddy recoiled but not from pain. During the cleaning, Buddy expressed his annoyance by mouthing hateful words. He resented being the object of care. During his career, Buddy had locked up criminals, defended the infirm, and protected the vulnerable. Now, Buddy was infirm and vulnerable. Just as with Dave, I represented an unpleasant reality to Buddy. Instead of misery, I represented despair. My presence reminded Buddy that he was a shell of his former self. The once rugged, tough crime fighter was a fragile, frail man who now fought only depression.

About a month after Dave and Buddy entered the nursing home, a thought occurred to me. *What an unsightly pair!* Dave and Buddy were both unpleasant men not because of their physical scars but because of their attitudes. I understood their anger, but after a month of acclimating to the nursing home and each other,

I thought their anger would dissipate. Dave and Buddy were two strangers who contrasted each other in many ways but also had similarities. Dave and Buddy were from different generations. They had different ethnicities, and they had different social communities. Dave had no family. Buddy had too many to count. Buddy had lived a full life. Dave's life was just getting started. Oddly, cancer had leveled these disparities. Naively, I thought sharing a room would mitigate the animosity both of these gentlemen felt. But neither of them wanted comfort nor to interact. I had no treatment or therapy that could cure them. However, I did have access to some of the best medicine on the planet.

CURTAINS UP

Dave and Buddy's double-occupancy room consisted of two sides that mirrored each other. Each side had a bed with a two-drawer night stand next to it. Adjacent to the night stand on the wall was a cork board containing a calendar and other information. Opposite the night stand and against the other wall was a small half-closet where a few pieces of linen and clothing could be stored. Separating the two sides was a cotton blend curtain. These curtains stretched the entire length of the room but were usually bundled tightly against the wall. In Dave and Buddy's room, the curtain remained extended. Neither one of them wanted to see or communicate with the other. It was disappointing. Dave continuously shooed people away out of anger. Buddy yelled endlessly at everyone. The staff avoided the pair, and I grew despondent. I didn't expect caregiving to be as thankless as it was. I also knew the feeling of despondency was an early warning sign of burnout, but I didn't know what to do. What I did know was that change needed to happen. The unusual pairing presented a perfect opportunity for two men in similar situations to build a relationship and face their anger issues. It was time for a dose of life's best medicine.

MAKE 'EM LAUGH

One afternoon I marched down the hallway, opened the door to Dave and Buddy's room, and positioned myself strategically between their two beds. I stood at the end of the curtain facing both gentlemen. The curtain hung directly in front of me separating the two sides of the room. Each one could see me, but neither could see the other. Then I began an improvisational stand-up routine. I cracked one joke after another. I told one entertaining story followed by another. Dave and Buddy were not amused. Every funny quip or lighthearted remark was met with stares and the familiar cricket sounds. *Tough room!* I thought. It's a tricky thing, dealing with life and death. There is nothing funny about facing your demise, but being able to find the sunbeams of humor in a darkened room can provide enough relief to change a perspective.

I kept going. I tried self-deprecating humor, annoying observations, and funny anecdotes one after another. At one point, Buddy tilted his head to one side like a dog trying to decipher human language. *These guys must think I'm nuts*, I thought. *At least neither one is yelling or telling me to leave. It's a start!* Undeterred, I continued. "Did you hear about the guy who ..." I said. "A funny thing happened last week when I ..." I continued. Finally, after what seemed like ten minutes of blank stares, something strange happened.

Out of the corner of my eye, I saw Dave's bed shaking. The sheets that covered his face trembled, and the top of his head quivered in unison. Intrigued, I walked over to Dave's bed, slowly pulled back the bed sheet and saw it, a laugh. "Ah ha!" I shouted. "I knew you had it in you!" For the first time since Dave was admitted to the nursing facility, I saw him smile. I savored the moment. A breakthrough had occurred. Dave experienced happiness. He expressed enjoyment. While I soaked up the moment, another sound emerged on the other side of the curtain.

I pulled back the curtain and glanced at Buddy. He had no scowl and no disdain on his face. His head was tilted slightly back, and his hands were on his belly. Like Dave, Buddy was laughing. I just couldn't hear it. Buddy's electronic speech device was out of arm's reach. His giddiness was inaudible. All I heard was air rushing in and out of Buddy's neck in an effort to keep up with Buddy's respiratory demands.

I wondered which story or joke caused the laughter. Maybe my delivery improved over time, or maybe it was a cumulative effect of all the humor presented. Most likely, Dave and Buddy laughed more at me than what I said. Who wouldn't be amused at the absurdity of my persistence and determination? The cause was irrelevant. The effect was not. Dave and Buddy finally shared a moment. The curtain had been pulled back, literally and figuratively. For a brief instance, their terminal illness didn't matter. Their impending death was unimportant. Their scars, vulnerability, and feebleness were immaterial. Dave and Buddy finally experienced a reprieve from their anger, and I felt satisfaction. But there was an unheeded danger associated with my comedic medicine.

COUGH CONFETTI

A strange thing happens to someone with an artificial airway when they laugh. They cough. Laughing is an excellent tool for pulmonary hygiene. It forces patients to expel unwanted secretions out of their airway. Usually, I welcome this conduct. However, I was standing in a room with two human spit wad shooters.

Before I could take a bow and thank my two-man audience, Dave and Buddy began showering the room with cough confetti. Like roses thrown on stage after a great performance, sputum started raining down from the two-member audience.

"For the love of all that is good and sterile, cover up your airways!" I pleaded. I felt like I was in the middle of a mucous war zone. "Shots fired, shots fired. RT in need of assistance!" I said to myself. As a result, I ducked for cover. This reaction only made matters worse. With my hands over my head, I looked everywhere for shelter. This child-like movement caused Dave and Buddy to laugh even harder.

The safest place to avoid being pepper sprayed by mucous is at the head of the bed. But as I moved ungracefully toward this apparent no spray zone, Dave and Buddy followed me with their eyes. Necks, and subsequently airways, tend to move in conjunction with one's eyes. I felt like I was caught in the laser focus of snipers shooting sputum. It was the most beautiful, unsanitary moment in my career.

CURTAIN CALL

From that day forward, Dave and Buddy tolerated each other's presence. They didn't become the best of friends, but they did permit the curtain separating the two halves of their room to remain open. Dave refused fewer treatments and Buddy yelled slightly less vigorously. The staff warmed up to the two as well, and I regained some joy that had waned during their care.

Several weeks later, Dave succumbed to his illness. He spent his last days in the nursing facility without ever going home. He never spent a day completely free of pain, but at least he had one moment when he didn't care about it.

Buddy progressed during his stay. After Dave passed, Buddy allowed his family to bear the brunt of his care. Weeks later, we discharged Buddy home. I never saw Buddy again, but I often wondered if he ever flooded his house with happy secretions as he had with me.

REEL TO REAL

In the movie *Anger Management*, a teacher uses unorthodox means such as confronting past bullies, pairing anger buddies together, and moving in with the client to address anger issues. Similarly, I chose a somewhat unorthodox presentation of laughter as a way of dealing with Dave and Buddy's seemingly endless frustration. Laughing had provided Dave and Buddy with a moment of levity that soothed their souls and helped manage their anger. Two strangers expressed enjoyment and set aside their cares and concerns. Laughter provided a momentary relief from their stress.

Laughter also gave me a tool to manage my potential burnout. When I have a stressful day, I intentionally look for something that makes me laugh. I might listen to one of my favorite stand-up comedians, watch a slapstick comedy, or recall a funny memory. When I do, stress melts away, and relief covers me like a fleece blanket. I also found that humor protected me from the daily stresses of working in medicine and helped me manage my anger. Taking brief moments for "laugh breaks" during a workday felt like wearing a protective rain jacket, which upon reflection, would have come in handy during my stand-up routine in Dave and Buddy's room!

SMOKE SCREEN TEST

Are you noticing that you are more cynical? Do you complain more now than you did in the past? These are signs that you're burning more fuel than you are replenishing. Try taking laugh breaks to break the pessimistic cycle.

Laughing provides physiological benefits to mitigate stress.

CHAPTER 2

WEEKEND AT BERNIE'S

THE TWO STUDENTS WAITED for their opportunity to treat real patients. Both sat quietly and patiently. Up to this point, their learning consisted of sitting in a classroom listening to lectures about gas physics, pulmonary anatomy, and pharmacology. The moment had arrived to put their knowledge to practice. I would be their clinical instructor for the day. The two students accompanying me had begun learning more advanced skills, and I wanted to take advantage of the interesting patients residing in this facility.

A sub-acute care nursing facility (SNF) holds some of the most curious and demanding patients in all healthcare settings. SNFs are the home of the chronic and long-term needs patients. Some of the patients are in persistent vegetative states unable to inter-act with their environments. Others are alert and communicate incessantly much to the provider's chagrin. Some patients breathe on their own, others need mechanical support. SNFs have it all. Where else can you be cursed out and called names you have never heard before by someone unable to phonate because they are on a ventilator? It's like being yelled at by a mime. Thus, there was no shortage of interesting patients.

Teaching was my favorite part of the job. It provided a niche in my job that mitigated stress. Patients' lives frequently rest in clinicians' hands. I wanted the students to learn properly and safely. I greeted the students and discussed the day ahead. I told them that the clinical practicum was about hands-on experience. Today, they would be the clinicians with all the responsibilities that come with that. Caregiving is serious business. The classroom served as preparation for real-life healthcare situations. Little did I know how wrong that statement was. Sometimes the real world produces a scenario so ridiculous and so unexpected that no amount of classroom teaching could provide the proper preparation. Today was that day.

HOW ABOUT I LAY YOU OUT?

The morning began like every other day. I drove in to work before sunrise. Only late-night party-goers, graveyard shift personnel, and I were on the streets. I arrived at work lethargic and desirous of finishing my shift so I could crawl back into the welcoming comfort of my bed. I received the report from my night-shift colleague, organized my assignment, and started preparing myself mentally for the twelve-hour workday, which meant closing my eyes for an extra five minutes. During my "meditation," my boss walked into the department and reminded us that two Respiratory students would be joining us. "Who wants to teach today?" she asked.

"I'll do it," I responded almost reflexively. I always volunteered to teach. Teaching was always a passion of mine. It was a core value for me, and whenever the opportunity arose to teach, I took advantage of it. The question was who were the best patients for the students to see for the most effective learning experience. Initially, I thought Larry would be the most interesting patient. With his colorful past, I knew he would stand out.

Larry was a young man with his whole life ahead of him. He was tall and athletic. He resembled the guy who could play any sport he wanted. I pictured Larry sitting at home seeing coaches from every major college in thirty-minute intervals. I imagined every university sending their best representative to recruit Larry to play football, basketball, or run track and field. His biggest dilemma would be to decide which school to attend. It would be a free ride for Larry. Sadly, that story never materialized. The real story was bleaker.

One day Larry's neighbor, Richard, caught Larry in, how shall we say, a compromising position with Richard's wife. Apparently, this was not the first time this occurred, and Richard had had enough. Richard reached out for assistance from his companion, Mr. Winchester, who was ready and willing to help. Larry noticed Richard and his hand-held friend and decided to forego any introduction. With all the athletic prowess he could muster, Larry fled the scene as fast as he could. Mr. Winchester was not worried. As Larry sprinted away, Richard fired his iron companion and peppered Larry's back with nine pellets at nearly point blank range. Larry survived, barely. He suffered a fracture of the first cervical vertebrae, rendering him unable to use any of his limbs or his diaphragm. Richard went to prison. Larry went to our SNF. The courts sentenced Richard to life without parole. Richard sentenced Larry to life without control. For the rest of his life, Larry would be dependent on the ventilator to breathe.

Larry barked orders at staff like an angry dog. He demanded his pillow be fluffed. He ordered his television channel changed, and he required his fingers to be positioned a specific width apart. Larry could do nothing for himself. He had no control over anything except being able to tell people what to do. I don't blame him—what a devastating reality. To be so young, helpless, and utterly dependent on others for care would make anyone cling to something they could control. Some argued he deserved what he got. I claimed the notion was irrelevant. My job was to care for him, regardless of circumstance.

Larry was the kind of patient I wanted the students to see. I wanted to know how the students would treat a patient who demands everything but can't speak. I wanted to discover how good they were at reading lips and how they would respond to a patient who continually swears, forcing the ventilator to alarm as if it was trying to censor the profanity. I wanted to challenge the students, but then I thought Larry might be too much of a test to start. The learning experience might be best served starting with a less complicated patient.

IS THIS NORMAL?

Mr. Parker would be my introductory patient. Mr. Parker destroyed his lungs through years of smoking. He had chronic lung disease and, like many of the patients, required a ventilator to breathe. Mr. Parker differed from other patients in one key area: his attitude. Mr. Parker welcomed every therapy and every staff member. He was polite and courteous. Every person who entered his room was greeted with a smile. Every intervention was followed by a "thank you." Mr. Parker was a gentleman. I imagined Mr. Parker walking down London streets in a top hat and coattails, carrying a walking stick to complete the ensemble. I pictured him tipping his hat ever so slightly as a courtesy to every lady who caught his eye. You couldn't help but address him as "sir." The title fit him. Physically, Mr. Parker was unassuming. He was well under six feet tall and was thin. But he looked healthy, not what you'd expect from a life-long smoker. Partly because of his mindset, Mr. Parker progressed to the point where he only needed the ventilator at night to breathe adequately. He commented he felt liberated during the day because he was not tethered to a machine. Unfortunately, a routine chest x-ray revealed a small growth in the left lower lobe of his lung. Despite his co-morbidities, doctors suggested removing the tumor. His physician scheduled a thoracotomy, an incision to open up the chest to access the lung and remove the tumor. After a week at the hospital, Mr. Parker returned to the SNF no worse for wear, at least physically.

A few days before the students arrived, I went to see Mr. Parker. He did not greet me with his cordial hello. His posture was hunched, and he stared vacantly out the window. "Are you ready for therapy?" I asked Mr. Parker, expecting his usual eager response. I received only a small nod in reluctant agreement. I hesitated taking Mr. Parker off the vent for a breathing trial. He wasn't smiling and he moved begrudgingly. Everyone has tough days, but Mr. Parker's entire countenance seemed to have changed since his surgery. He continued to say "thank you" and never refused therapy, but he made less eye contact. It was if the surgeons had accidentally removed his enthusiasm and drive along with his tumor. I thought seeing new faces and helping future therapists would benefit Mr. Parker.

I took the students to see Mr. Parker. The first student, Gwen, took exceptional notes. She was in her early twenties and anxious to learn as much as she could, because she knew she would be responsible for caring for patients on her own in just a few short months. She realized learning to manage patients correctly started here. Paul, the other student, was very similar to Gwen both in age and mindset. Unlike Gwen, Paul didn't take notes. He observed. Both were attentive listeners and grasped concepts easily. I was blessed to have both of them together on the same day.

I wouldn't be Gwen and Paul's only teacher. Mr. Parker would instruct us as well. His room was our classroom. His life was our textbook. His lungs demonstrated the consequences of smoking. His ventilator revealed the incredible advancement of technology, and his attitude taught us that even the most positive among us have days of doubt and frustration. My goal was threefold: 1) to help the students understand the basics of pulmonary disease management in a safe environment, 2) to remind the students the critical role Respiratory Therapists (RTs) play in the often over-looked chronic patient demographics, and 3) possibly to return Mr. Parker's positive outlook on life. I knew the last one would be the most difficult. Surgery had changed Mr. Parker. As we began our session, little did I know another situation would arise that would completely derail any chance of accomplishing my goals.

As Gwen, Paul, and I discussed ventilators, airways, and lung disease, we noticed a commotion on the other side of the room. Mr. Parker shared his room with another patient, Mr. Lomax. I knew very little about Mr. Lomax as he had no pulmonary issues and was not on my caseload. The commotion grew louder and more feverish. The students and I could not see precisely what was occurring because another clinician had drawn the curtain. Every double occupant room had as part of its decor a drab, green colored curtain. The curtains were old and frequently smelly because staff rarely changed them. They were long and extended from the ceiling to about eight inches above the floor. This eight-inch space was our only window to what was happening. First, we saw two sets of Nikes. Then a pair of adidas joined the group. One couple left, then two pairs of Danskos arrived. Every new pair of shoes entered more abruptly and with greater urgency. Also, the tone of the conversation changed. The commotion started as a whisper but increased in intensity when the latest pair of shoes entered the room. The students were mesmerized. I tried explaining the nuances of ventilator settings, but the students blocked me out. They just stared at brand-name footwear.

"What's going on?" Paul asked.

"I'm not sure. It's probably nothing," I said unconvincingly. As I tried to dismiss the distraction, I noticed something different about one pair of shoes under the curtain. Blue scrub pants accompanied this pair of shoes. Only Respiratory Therapists wore blue pants in this facility. I thought this was odd because Mr. Lomax did not need Respiratory Therapy. Why was an RT part of this brouhaha?

At this point, I stopped teaching. I too was transfixed. The students and I stood quietly and tried to decipher the apparent confusion that persisted just a few feet away. Even Mr. Parker turned his head in curiosity. All we needed was popcorn and stadium seating and this could have been a theatrical matinee. Suddenly, the plot changed. Two pairs of shoes began pushing the bed closer to the wall while another pair of shoes pulled in a geriatric chair. The "Geri chair" is ideal for patients who need to sit up for therapy, comfort, or other care. The chairs recline and are a great alternative to sitting up in the bed. But they are large and take up a lot of space. I thought, *Why do this now? And what is the urgency?*

The fracas grew more intense. *This is insane*, I thought. The suspense was killing me. Seeing that I had completely lost the attention of my students and realizing I couldn't maintain focus, I finally broke my silence. "What the heck are you guys doing?" I inquired.

Suddenly the curtain flew back and the RT responded emphatically, "Mr. Lomax expired, and we're placing him in a Geri chair!"

A hush filled the room. Everybody stared, including me. That response did not explain anything. It only created more confusion. The students tried to interpret the scene. Their eyebrows drew close together, and their eyes narrowed. Unable to find any memory file from their classroom or textbook that could explain such a response, Gwen looked at me and asked, "Is this normal?"

I was at a loss. Nothing computed. As professionally as I could and without turning my eyes away from the scene, I responded, "Uh, no." Unsatisfied with my own reply, I interrupted the commotion and asked a clarifying question. "So, the patient is dead?"

"Yes," the RT responded matter-of-factly without another word of detail. Because none of the responses from the peanut gallery on the other side of the curtain appeased my curiosity, I decided to table my professionalism briefly.

"But 'expired' and 'Geri chair' do not belong in the same sentence!" I said extremely sarcastically.

"Look," the RT replied impatiently, "Mr. Lomax died a while ago. We contacted the funeral home, and they were supposed to take Mr. Lomax. However, we discovered the large front elevator is broken. The only other elevator available is located in the back. But the back elevator is too small to fit a bed or the funeral home's gurney. The only thing we can use is a Geri chair. Unfortunately, to get to that elevator, we have to roll Mr. Lomax past the dining area. It is now lunchtime. As you know, some of the patients have dementia and others are emotionally unstable, and if they see a dead body rolling past them, there will be chaos. Therefore, the only way to get Mr. Lomax out of the facility and avoid the chaos that a dozen wailing geriatrics can cause is to put him in a Geri chair, pretend he's alive, and wheel him by the other residents in a way not to provoke suspicion."

As frightening as this sounds, it actually makes sense, I thought.

"Oh my gosh," Gwen blurted. "It's *Weekend at Bernie's*!" Paul and I and all the other people in the room stopped, stared, and contemplated the remark. Obviously, we had all seen the movie since we all were nodding our heads.

"She's right. It is *Weekend at Bernie's*," I said. In that film, two friends attempt to maintain the illusion that their deceased boss is alive by taking him on trips and excursions, including driving him around in a golf cart.

"What's next? Are you going to tie a string to Mr. Lomax's arm and pull it as you pass another resident?" I questioned. "Maybe put a nasal cannula in his nose, you know, to keep up appearances?" Everyone chuckled. It seemed a little inappropriate to make light of the situation. A patient had passed away. He was someone's son, father, and friend. But the circumstance was absurd! If only we had a golf cart to transport Mr. Lomax.

After the scene, serious education flew out the window. I could not compete with such a debacle. Both goal number one and two had seemingly disappeared. I was somewhat disappointed. I wanted the learning experience to begin with Mr. Parker, an easy, welcoming patient and end with Larry, a difficult, stubborn patient. I wanted the students to be exposed to the entire range of the patient population and realize the critical role that RTs played. Instead, I had been part of a scenario only screenwriters could create. But Gwen and Paul loved it. After only a few hours at the SNF, they had a lifelong story to share with their classmates and instructors that no one could top. As I signed the student's paperwork and wished them luck in their future careers, Gwen shook my hand and said, referring to Mr. Lomax, "What a day! Only an RT could come up with an idea like that."

I decided she was right. I guess my initial reaction was wrong. The students did achieve goal number two.

Because of the *Weekend at Bernie's* episode, I briefly forgot about Mr. Parker. After the dust settled, I went to check on him. He had lost a roommate. Although they never interacted, one can't help but reflect on one's own mortality when someone passes away. Patients sometimes regress and withdraw for a couple of days as they mourn and grieve. I wanted to see how Mr. Parker was coping.

I entered the room and saw Mr. Parker in good spirits. He was in the best frame of mind since his surgery. "How are you, Mr. Parker?" I asked.

"Good," he responded. "What's next for therapy?"

"Nothing else today," I said. "I thought the chaos from earlier might be enough therapy for now. If you don't mind me saying, you seem to be in a better mood. What's different?"

"What's different?" Mr. Parker asked in surprise. "The events earlier were surreal," he continued. "The fact that you people went through all that just to spare some of the residents some heartache is incredible. I'm still alive, so what's next?" He was right. The staff went above and beyond anything they were expected to do, albeit in a bizarre way. I had taken their efforts for granted, but

Mr. Parker had not. I enjoyed seeing the old Mr. Parker back. His positive outlook had returned, just as I'd hoped. Two out of three goals ain't bad.

REEL TO REAL

In the movie *Weekend at Bernie's*, two friends go to great lengths to convince others that their expired boss is still alive. Fearing for their lives from a hitman and taking advantage of the opportunity to enjoy their boss's luxurious beach house, the two friends take their dead boss to the beach, on a boat, and drive him around in a golf cart. Their charade works. No one is aware that Bernie has passed.

Weekend at Bernie's is an absurd movie. There is no moral to the story and no profound message delivered. The movie is goofy and ridiculous. In other words, it's fun. The incident involving Mr. Parker, his roommate, and the students reminded me how bizarre caregiving can be.

Working in healthcare involves contact with blood, needles, germs, wounds, and a litany of other things that would send a large part of the population into a lifetime of mental therapy. The job is stressful and fosters burnout. Finding your niche helps keep the burnout gremlins at bay. Teaching was my niche. It made the stressful days manageable and caregiving enjoyable. As the situation with Mr. Lomax and the students demonstrated to me, every situation can be a teaching moment. And, if you're lucky, some of those moments may provide future illustrations for students. When I'm asked to recall the craziest scenario I've seen, I reply the same way, "Have you ever seen the movie *Weekend at Bernie's*?"

SMOKE SCREEN TEST

Have you had moments when you questioned your career choice? Do you like the field you are in but dislike your specific job? Are there parts of your job that you really enjoy? If so, consider working in a different area of your field. Often, it's not the vocation of healthcare that burns us out but a particular aspect of it. Seek niches that emphasize the aspects of your job that you really enjoy and minimize those areas you don't.

Finding your niche in your workplace can decrease stress.

CHAPTER 3

THE BUCKET LIST

EVERY MORNING VIRGINIA WOKE up to the same scene: a view of a brick wall outside her window, the sound of snoring from her roommate, and the persistent odor of a diaper in desperate need of changing. The scene tortured her senses. Where were the palm trees for her eyes to enjoy? Where was the sound of the ocean for her ears? And why hasn't someone invested in potpourri!? "Jim," she said one day, "I can't stand this place."

"What do you mean?" I asked.

"It's the same thing every day," she said. "The food never changes. I get the same medicine, and you give me the same treatments four times a day."

"I can't argue with that," I replied. "By the way, here's your treatment." Virginia gave me a look of disgust. Begrudgingly, she took the medicine that was supposed to open up her lungs to improve her breathing. We both knew the treatment provided little benefit.

Every day in Virginia's life was now monotonous and repetitive, which differed significantly from her earlier life. The stark contrast between what now seemed like two completely separate lives only heightened her dismay at her present situation. She wished she could return to her past, but that was not an option. The mundaneness would persist unless she found a way to change it.

MEET VIRGINIA

I met Virginia soon after I started working in the skilled nursing facility. Virginia needed continual pulmonary interventions because of her disease. Alpha-1 Antitrypsin Deficiency had ravaged her body, rendering it weak and debilitated. The genetic disorder stiffened her lungs, making them resemble those of an eighty-year-old chain smoker. Her petite stature and small face hid behind the swelling that came from years of prescribed steroid use, leaving her with the characteristic "moon-face." Like so many other diseases, Alpha-1 robbed Virginia of future memories. It robbed her of having a husband and kids. It robbed her of the experience of family vacations, job promotions, and wedding anniversaries. In short, it robbed her of time. Time, Virginia always thought, she had in abundance. And it robbed her of little things too. Comforting a child when they fell, enjoying great movies at the theater, and eating a lavish dinner she couldn't afford were experiences Virginia would never have. Instead, Virginia would spend her final days in a nursing home surrounded by sights and smells she never imagined existed. And she was only forty years old.

"What do you do when you're not here?" Virginia asked as she was taking her treatment.

"Not much," I replied. "I read, watch movies, and work out."

"I could tell you work out," she replied, smiling. "What kind of movies do you like? What kind of books do you read?" I welcomed the questions. I thought they were Virginia's attempt at breaking the tediousness of her day, and it was nice having a conversation with her. But before I could answer, Virginia interrupted me. "It's not fair," she said. "There is so much life I have yet to live. There is so much I still want to do, and believe me, I've already done a lot!"

Virginia meant what she said. A bevy of stories from her past usually accompanied every breathing treatment I administered. Virginia described her previous lifestyle in surprising, often graphic, detail. Virginia worked in the music industry. "All of those rumors about the rock and roll lifestyle are true," she boldly proclaimed. "I worked with many bands over the years. I helped them with their instruments, travel arrangements, even booked some gigs. I was essentially a small-town roadie. I helped bands with whatever they needed and sometimes with whatever they wanted," she said emphatically. Virginia did not mince words. She had no filter and had a vocabulary that, well, you would expect from living a rock and roll lifestyle. I think Virginia enjoyed shocking me with her exploits because she got a kick out of making me uncomfortable. Over time, I began to appreciate her brashness. I found it refreshing; others didn't.

"Virginia has a mouth on her," a coworker said one day. "She just told me a story about one of her escapades with some band she toured with. I can't repeat what she said, but I was the one who left the room blushing." I smiled because I could see Virginia getting pleasure out of making someone blush.

It came time to administer the next round of treatments to Virginia. I thought I would preempt any monotony by asking her a question. "Do you have any regrets?" I asked as I prepared her inhalation cocktail.

"Of course, who doesn't?" she answered. "I was not the poster child of propriety. I had very few scruples. But I sure had fun. I guess my biggest regret is finding out about my disease so late. Now I am physically unable to check off most of the items on my bucket list."

Virginia did not exaggerate. Alpha-1 imprisoned her. Air flowed into her lungs unencumbered but seeped out of her lungs slowly. Alpha-1 Deficiency obstructed her airflow. The disease destroyed the walls of the alveoli, the sites of gas exchange, rendering them useless. Air could not get out of her lungs efficiently. Physiologically, she had emphysema. Practically, she could not breathe. Every breath corresponded to exercise. Walking to the bathroom required preparation. Eating became a chore. Some days sitting up carried the same effects as running a marathon. The disease forced her to rely on others for assistance. But Virginia had no immediate family. She had no loved ones she could lean on for support. Residing in a skilled nursing facility was her only option. She resigned herself to accept that she would live her final days in the care of strangers. And those last days fast approached.

I periodically thought about regrets. If I knew I would die tomorrow would I have any regrets? I agreed with Virginia. We all have regrets, but mine were inconsequential. I had no bucket list. I had accomplished everything I set out to do. Moving forward merely brought new aspirations. I've always been ambitious and impatient. When I had a goal, I ran toward it. I didn't like to waste time. Many people say it's not the goal that is important but the journey. There is truth to that, but there is also satisfaction knowing you accomplished something you set out to do.

SUPPOSED TO BE FUN

Virginia's story stood out. Her situation provoked an unexpected level of compassion in me. If I were in her position, how would I feel? Moreover, because I am not, is there anything I can do to help Virginia? Nothing came to mind.

When Virginia first came to the nursing home, I spent extra time with her. Over the next months I spent less and less. My intention was there, but my commitment wasn't. I rationalized my absence by telling myself that other patients needed me equally or I was too busy, but the truth was I lost the desire to see Virginia. Watching her deteriorate took its toll.

Accepting the inability to restore a patient's health is liberating in one sense. I knew the only thing I could do for Virginia was keep her comfortable. Chronic diseases also bring disappointment and a sense of failure. Virginia's condition sapped the joy out of caregiving and caused me to become emotionally calloused. I grew numb with the constant emotional pounding of death and illness. This numbness prevented me from showing compassion and empathy, qualities that patients desperately need from their caregivers. I feared spending too much time with Virginia would cause me to develop untreatable calcifications, at least that is what I told myself.

Months passed and, as expected, Virginia's health declined. She no longer could breathe without supplemental oxygen. Though she maintained her wits and brazenness, she told fewer stories. She did not have the energy. The end-stages of her genetic disorder arrived without fail. But I thought I had failed as well. I failed to help Virginia in any meaningful way. Although I empathized with Virginia and listened to her stories, I was unable to show her the amount of compassion she needed. I had no allusions to restoring her health, but I could have comforted her by providing more opportunities to share her regrets. I could have just listened to her. But I had grown tired of seeing Virginia's health decline, and I even avoided treating her when I could. Guilt rose up like acid reflux. Something needed to change, not the least of which was my attitude. I should have done more, but I didn't want to sit in Virginia's room and pretend to listen. She would see right through me. She would accept no pity. I had no answers. Little did I know, Virginia did.

As Virginia's health declined, my job morphed into filling out paperwork that measured how quickly Virginia's life was fading away. She needed increasingly more oxygen. She had less lung reserve. She required higher doses of medications, and her functionality decreased. But Virginia resisted giving up, and inklings of life remained. She refused to lie in bed and wait to die. She would take whatever joyride life had left. Unknowingly, I would ride shotgun.

FINDING THE JOY

One day the nurse called and said Virginia wanted to see me. Virginia rarely requested my company because I saw her every few hours anyway. If she called, something was usually wrong. When I arrived at her door, Virginia was visibly upset. "Jim, fix this *#$!! ear-piercing noise coming from my oxygen tubing," Virginia demanded. "It's driving me crazy!" Immediately, I located the problem. Part of Virginia's tubing had lodged under the wheel of the oxygen concentrator. The weight of the machine's wheel obstructed the flow from the concentrator to her nose—an ironic situation considering the nature of her disease. This caused the oxygen to squeal like air slowly escaping from a balloon. Equipment issues are not uncommon. What was not commonplace was what Virginia did next.

"I see the problem," I responded almost immediately. "The tubing is kinked under the wheel. Just give me a second, and I'll fix it." Virginia's tubing was over twenty feet long. The long length provided ample room for Virginia to walk without feeling tethered to one area of the room, but it also increased the chances of getting tangled. I walked over to the concentrator and bent over to lift the wheel off the tubing. But just as I started pulling the untangled plastic away from the concentrator, I felt the force of a blacksmith's grip on my rump. Virginia had clutched the right side of my derriere! She did not pinch me with a couple of fingers nor did she graze the back of her hand against my tush. Virginia latched on to the whole right side of my keister with the full force of Lebron James preparing to dunk a basketball!

"What in the world are you doing?" I asked as I quickly made myself upright.

With complete indifference and without any signs of remorse, Virginia replied stoically, "I'm dying. If an opportunity like that presents itself, I'm going to take advantage of it." For several seconds, I just stared at her with my jaw dropped. Virginia stared back at me, unmoved by the situation. Neither one of us spoke. We locked eyes. I felt torn. On one level, Virginia had no excuse for her actions. On another level, I had to admit Virginia had a point. When death is near, conventional boundary lines blur.

After a brief stand-off, I reassessed the situation. Based on

Virginia's medical diagnosis and her unwavering resolve, I conceded Virginia's actions and replied with two words, "Fair enough." Virginia nodded in agreement. A slight grin emerged on her face like a whole new world of possibilities had materialized. Her ordinary day could now be a thing of the past. Her eyes narrowed as she considered her options. I feared where her mind was taking her, and I refused to ask. With Virginia's background, personality, and ever-increasing blurred moral boundaries, I decided to keep a safe distance. I backed up a few more feet and gave Virginia another stern look. Sensing everything was back to normal, except for the palm print that would reside on my butt a few more days, I started to leave. Virginia stopped me and asked me a question. "May I borrow your pen?" she asked.

"Yes," I responded, slightly concerned. "But why?" Reaching into her bedside drawer, Virginia pulled out a notepad with writing on it.

"You were number seven on my bucket list," Virginia said with great satisfaction. With that remark, Virginia finally smiled.

BRINGING JOY TO OTHERS

About two weeks after my basketball incident, Virginia succumbed to her disease. She passed away peacefully with, apparently, one less item left on her list. As I thought about the palm print that still felt as if it remained on my backside, I wondered if I was really on Virginia's bucket list. *Probably not*, I thought. *Virginia was having whatever fun she could in her last days.* I'm sure she shared that story with whomever she could. I'm also certain she laughed when she shared it. But her surprising exploit taught me something. I should always take advantage of every opportunity and, if possible, bring joy to others in the process. Life is too short to worry about menial things. However, Virginia's life was no menial thing. I could have done more. Virginia craved anything that would interrupt the ordinary cycle of her day. I could have provided a welcomed change from the boring view of her window, her tasteless food, or at least purchased some potpourri. But I didn't. I chose to spend more time away from Virginia than with her.

Virginia also showed me something I later learned in seminary. Guilt can be objective and subjective. Objective guilt occurs when we break laws, legally or morally. Subjective guilt is the feeling of being guilty, whether we are or not. Though I felt guilty for not spending more time with Virginia, Virginia took no offense. She understood. I had not broken any promise or commitment to her. I only had a subjective feeling that I could have done more. This powerful feeling could have festered for months had Virginia not "handled" the situation. Her outrageous action put things into perspective, causing the guilt I felt to dissipate.

REEL TO REAL

Patients like Virginia provoke reflection. In the movie *The Bucket List*, two guys meet in a cancer ward where they are both treated. Realizing their deaths are imminent, they decide to live their final days crossing off things on their bucket list such as visiting the Taj Mahal and the Great Wall of China and going skydiving. Along the way, they reflect, learn life lessons, and remember the important things in life. Similarly, remembering Virginia's life, her bucket list, and her outrageous behavior helped quell my guilt that could have led to burnout. Her perseverance to change her dull day into something memorable also reminded me to concentrate on things that matter. It's easy to forget the reason for going into the caregiving field. Most, including me, ventured into healthcare to help others. In time, the repetitive patient load and population can be emotionally draining. Taking time to remember the impact I've had on patients and, more profoundly, the effect they have had on me refuels the depleted tank. To refuel a gasoline tank, the driver needs to stop, pull over, and take the necessary time to fill up. Likewise, recalling the reasons for entering the caregiving field forces us to pause and gives us time to fill our empty compassion tanks. But one thing continued to bother me for years after that incident. If Virginia did not make up the fact that I was on her bucket list, why was I number seven? Surely, my butt deserved a higher ranking!

SMOKE SCREEN TEST

Do you feel your job has transformed into a list of tasks that need completed? Do you find yourself counting the hours until the weekend? Have you forgotten why you chose to go into your particular field? Write down why you chose your particular vocation, then post it in a place where you constantly see it. Every few months change the location of the paper so you don't get used to it and overlook it.

Remembering why you chose your field can help you
focus your attention on the important things.

CHAPTER 4

BURNT

I STARED AT THE back of the man's shirt. *He has a lot of dandruff*, I thought. *He should not be wearing black.* My gaze drifted to another person. "That purse is as large as she is!" I muttered. "She must have back problems." Every few minutes I fixated on another person and created their backstory to occupy my time. The man in front of me, I surmised, worked as a ski patroller because the white flakes on his shoulders resembled the snow-powdered slopes of the Vail Ski Resort in Colorado. His name will be Sven. Mrs. giant purse lady will be called Natalie. She will be a former QVC host whose severance package included a variety of goods never sold on the air. Next, I stared at the floor. *How many people have stood in this same spot before me?* I wondered. Then I turned around. *Those poor souls*, I thought. *It will take thirty minutes for them to reach the place in line where I am now.*

Perfecting the art of queuing takes practice. The process requires open inner dialogue, creative observation, and patience—a tool set I never thought I would be using in an unemployment line. I

41

had worked for three years in the pulmonary field. Did I make the wrong career choice? Could I not make it in medicine? If I failed at this, where else would I fall flat? The way I saw it, I had only two choices: wait in the unemployment line or stay at work. There was no dilemma. I couldn't stay at work. I couldn't take it anymore, not after last month.

A SERIES OF BAD CHOICES

I began working in the pulmonary field as a Respiratory student. I went to school from seven in the morning to three in the afternoon and worked from seven to eleven in the evening. Weekends consisted of twelve-hour shifts. Then the cycle continued. The non-stop rotation dragged on for over a year. I made little time for exercising and virtually no time for family and friends. All I did was work and study. I took no breaks.

I started working at a nearby SNF while I was a student. Aside from treating notoriously tricky patients, I had limited responsibilities. That is a euphemistic way of saying I was a pulmonary gofer. As a student, I lacked the credentials to perform more critical duties. Therefore, I became the expert in the mundane, the tedious, and the loathed aspects of care. When you combine long hours, no breaks, and mind-numbing working conditions, you get a recipe for disaster.

Burnout usually happens slowly. It's the result of a build-up of stressors that accumulate over time. Often, there is an instance you can pinpoint that broke the proverbial camel's back, as it were. For me, it wasn't an event. It was a person.

MR. JONES AND ME

Mr. Jones was one of the long-term residents I encountered just two years after graduating from respiratory school. He was a man of unparalleled determination and unwavering resolve. No matter who entered his room, no matter what assistance came his way, he invariably refused. When physical therapy wanted to start treatment, Mr. Jones refused. When the nurse dispensed his medication, he declined. When I asked him to wait until I finished treating another patient, he complained.

Mr. Jones was the laziest man I have ever met. Imagine a slug on Prozac bathing in a tub of Ativan. That was Mr. Jones. Because of his laziness, physicians placed a tracheostomy in his neck and connected him to the ventilator because he refused to move. As a result, Mr. Jones developed recurring bouts of pneumonia. His sole desire was to watch television and drool. He only moved when he requested suctioning.

"Mr. Jones, would you please wait another moment while I finish with this patient?" I asked on numerous occasions after being summoned into his room to care for his airway. Mr. Jones always shrugged in defiance. "Mr. Jones, would you at least wipe the saliva from your mouth?" I asked as he let a waterfall of mucous slide down his chin.

Mr. Jones shook his head back and forth signaling an emphatic no!

The staff tried every motivational approach to change his behavior. They tried the Joel Osteen way. "Mr. Jones, you know God loves you, and He wants you to get better. Let's honor Him by working together to get your best life … now." Mr. Jones responded by pointing to his airway for suctioning. Staff tried what I refer to as the Jerry McGuire approach. "Mr. Jones, we're here to help you, but you have to want to get better. Mr. Jones, help us help you. Show me the desire!" Mr. Jones only shrugged.

Staff also tried the tough love or drill sergeant approach, "Mr. Jones, you're a disgrace. Get out of that bed now, soldier! We are going to move it, move it, move it and so help me if you point to your trach again I will rip that finger off your hand and shove it down your PEG tube!"

Mr. Jones sat motionless and unfazed. Of course, no one was that harsh, but it speaks to the fact the nothing worked. There were dozens of other patients who would do anything to be in this man's condition. They were motivated and wanted to get healthy, and this man, who had no major chronic illness, was too lazy to do anything.

Moreover, Mr. Jones did not pay for his care. The federal government graciously used tax dollars to assist in his care. Mr. Jones came to represent everything that frustrated me about healthcare: accepting that some patients cannot be helped, government bureaucracy, and wasting one's life.

I consistently became less patient and more agitated. My level of compassion dwindled and my empathetic skills faded. Then one day, I snapped.

In an older facility, things inevitably break down. One day Tony, the maintenance man, responded to a request to fix a broken bed. Tony was a quiet man who kept to himself. He was tall and thin and had worked for the company for decades. To reach and replace the broken part, Tony needed the bed lifted. I volunteered to assist. The task was simple. Deadlift the foot of the bed while maintenance slides underneath to replace a loose bolt.

Lifting a bed sounds like the job description of a powerlifter, but when the bed is empty of a mattress and linen, it is anything but impressive.

While I was pretending to set the world deadlift record (which is 500 kg or 1,102 lbs!), I noticed a commotion out of the corner of my left eye. I hadn't realized the room with the broken bed was in sight of Mr. Jones's peering eye.

Mr. Jones watched me pick up the bed, then he tapped a plastic suction device against his bed rail for assistance. Without a modicum of consideration, Mr. Jones tapped persistently and relentlessly. "In a minute," I told Mr. Jones, slightly agitated since there was no medical urgency. He continued tapping. I kept holding the bed.

"Almost done," Tony said. Tap-tap-tap went the sound of plastic on the metal frame. "Just one more moment," Tony continued. The tap-tap-tapping came again. It was fingernails on a chalkboard—the sound that gets under your skin causing every nerve impulse to fire. Your head turns and your body twists trying to extinguish the annoyance. The build-up of the incessant tapping, my contorted figure, and the prolonged weight of the bed came to a climax. "There, all done," announced Tony. A split second afterward, everything erupted.

I slammed the bed down on the floor and walked abruptly across the hall. "Could you not see that I was busy!" I barked as I walked into Mr. Jones's room. "Do you not understand what 'in a minute' means?" I asked even louder. "You could get better, get off the vent, and go home if you chose to!" I continued. "But you're too lazy to do it. What's the matter with you?" I asked rhetorically as I shook my head. I wiped the man's chin, cleaned out his artificial airway, and walked out of the room. I knew there was a problem. Others did too. No one should react that way toward a patient. I lost control, but I couldn't help it.

People noticed my frustration and tried to help. Cliché advice spewed from everyone's lips. "Jim, it could be worse," one co-worker said. "At least you're getting paid!"

Have those words ever soothed a burned soul? I thought. Instead, the sentence exacerbates the issue. Not only am I angry, but now I feel guilty. And just because it could be worse does not mean it's not bad now!

Others would quip, "Jim, you care too much."

What a ridiculous statement! *Is that possible and what's the alternative? I thought. Care less or don't care at all? What a good anecdote for patient care! I can see the billboard advertisement now: Join the team at Careless Medical Center—you'll never burn out again.*

My tolerance level shrank. Agitation was my heartbeat. Exhaustion was my breath. Compassion was a distant memory. I fantasized about winning the lottery, living on a secluded mountaintop, and having a career that didn't cause me to grit my teeth with every thought. My emotional and physical state suffered. Patient care suffered too. Gone were the comic relief, the personal touches, and the enjoyment. All that remained were disgust, sorrow, and self-loathing. I did not have a remedy, but I persevered.

MAXED OUT

Teammates gave their assistance. If Mr. Jones appeared on my assignment, a co-worker would often take him. One considerate teammate was Max.

Max was from Latvia. He had the gentlest of dispositions. Always ready to lend a hand and assist, Max garnered the respect of everyone he encountered. He was a family man, humble, and kind-hearted. He had all the characteristics of the model caregiver, and nothing upset him, or so I thought.

Max spoke with a Russian-like accent. "You need relax," he would say. "Is ok. I take care of patient. No need worry for you." What an offer! I did not hesitate. I gladly released Mr. Jones from my caseload that day. I felt conflicted. Avoiding Mr. Jones brought some relief, but I should be able to handle difficult patients. I never had a problem before.

Just before lunch, I decided to check on Max. I discovered he was with Mr. Jones. I did not interrupt him but waited outside the room. Max had chosen to care for Jack, Mr. Jones's roommate, first.

Jack required simple care. A quick assessment and basic treatments were all he needed. Max could complete Jack's therapy in five minutes, leaving ample time to deal with Mr. Jones. Max greeted Mr. Jones and told him he would be with him after he treated Jack. Mr. Jones loathed the idea.

After Max started helping Jack, Mr. Jones's *modus operandi* began. Tap-tap-tap went the plastic against the bedrail. Followed by tap-tap-tap again. Max turned around and politely reminded Mr.

Jones that he would be with him soon. Mr. Jones remained steadfast. Tap-tap-tap again. Max turned around. "Mr. Jones, I tell you wait." Tap-tap-tap again. "Mr. Jones, you need be patient," Max replied with an even gentler voice. "No tap again, please."

With an undeterred resolve, Mr. Jones tapped a fifth time, this time non-stop. Suddenly, and without warning, Max erupted. "I tell you stop!" Max roared with a grizzly-like pitch. "I no tell you anymore!"

My jaw dropped. I had never heard Max lose his temper. I peeked in the room. Max stood over Mr. Jones with his back toward the door. All I could see was Mr. Jones's face. He looked terrified. Mr. Jones reacted as if his life might be in danger. Maybe it was. I walked up to Max slowly so as not to heighten an already volatile situation and because I was a little frightened too. When you back a bear into a corner, there is no telling what may happen. "Are you okay?" I asked Max as gently as I could.

"He no listen!" Max roared again. At this point, Max turned around, and I saw what Mr. Jones saw. Max's face glowed like hot coals under a fire. His eyes looked charcoal black, and he didn't blink for what seemed like minutes. Hell hath no fury like a Latvian scorned.

"Why don't we take a break?" I suggested to Max as I escorted him to the break room. Several minutes passed before Max calmed down. I let him vent and get his frustration out while I stood at a safe distance. When Max finished, I said, "Max, you've been Jonesed."

"What mean Jonesed?" Max asked.

"He got to you," I responded. "Mr. Jones finally pushed you over the edge. Welcome to the club." Max and I laughed about the idea for several minutes. Some patients have a way of finding that last nerve. Then they poke their finger on it until you snap. It was nice to know Max was human.

It comforted me to know that Mr. Jones had the same effect on others as he did on me. Misery loves company. But misery remained. I still felt drained, lethargic, and questioned whether I could continue working in a field that showed no potential for any significant change.

Burnout leaves a smelly residue that often takes a professional to abate. I looked for ways to reignite the flame. I took days off. I tried to peer at the proverbial bright side, and I made a point to exercise regularly. These adjustments briefly ignited the flame, but they had no lasting effect. I needed a change, something drastic. The change finally happened with a small piece of paper.

THE SMOKING TICKET

After graduating from respiratory school, I continued to work at the SNF. Over the next few years, I worked my way to a valued, full-time employee. One day bad news arrived. Without warning, the company decided to cut jobs. Each department would lose two to three positions. The staff drew back. We all knew low seniority positions would be eliminated first. Surprisingly, I was safe. With only three years in the field, I was a veteran. Notices of termination came down. Helene would be let go.

Helene had a family with two kids. Her income was essential.

She lived a modest lifestyle, no fancy cars, no luxurious house or extravagant vacations. Helene lived well within her means, a rarity in this age. She had no other options, no job prospects. Helene had only one day to prepare, and she hoped that she had just enough seniority to stay. Unfortunately, she didn't.

I felt saddened, but I understood the business decision. Either a few jobs were eliminated, or all of them were. Nagging me through this "transition" period of "restructuring" was the lingering smell of burnout. My situation remained unchanged though now, with fewer staff, work would be more demanding. *I can't believe my situation will be getting worse*, I thought as my mind quickly shifted from sympathy toward Helene to self-absorption. Then something happened that disrupted my thought. A nurse asked me a simple question, a common request, "Could you suction a patient?" Sounds of shattered glass and a record needle scratching an album's surface resonated in my head. *That's it*, I thought. *I can't do this anymore.*

I walked over to Helene, who remained visibly upset, and I asked for her pink slip. She was confused. "I'm leaving," I said. "I will take your place. Keep your position."

People were stunned. They labeled me a hero. I had exhibited amazing altruism and selflessness. "I can't believe you did that," people said. "You're so kind."

I wish all that were true. The reality was, I quit. I couldn't stand to work as an RT anymore. The pink slip served as an easy ticket out.

A SPARK IGNITED

I managed to make ends meet by tutoring middle and high school students for the next few months. Teaching was the environment where I thrived. Helping others grow and learn refueled me and always reignited the flame. When you find the niche where your values, passion, and mission align, you become fulfilled. Unfortunately, the income didn't last. Tutoring was only short-lived. When summer arrived, I had no students. No students meant no income. No income meant I had to cash in my pink slip.

So here I was, staring at people and inventing stories while waiting in line to speak to the unemployment officer. I reflected on the events that brought me here. I was exhausted, disappointed, and beaten. I had cared for everyone but myself. I let myself and others down. And I had been Jonesed. I had let a patient push me to my breaking point. I wanted to raise my head with the consolation that despite all the laziness and despite the lack of motivation to improve, Mr. Jones finally recovered. But I could not. Shortly after I left, Mr. Jones died. He died without trying. He died without being curious. He died without attempting to improve himself and others. He had lived a wasted life. With that thought, I shook my head in disgust.

Burnout had occurred slowly. The repetitive pounding of unmet expectations, rote tasks, and the wasted life of Mr. Jones extinguished the passionate flame I once had to care for patients. I realized I burned out because I didn't know my vulnerabilities. I didn't identify my strengths. I hadn't protected myself. As a result, I reevaluated my situation and chose to leave the profession, at least for a time. Surprisingly, losing my flame for medicine had a silver lining. My passion for teaching rekindled. I had to find some way of incorporating this more into my work if I were to reenter the field.

"Next, please," said the man behind the desk, breaking my concentration. I walked over and sat down in front of him. "What brings you in today?" asked the gentleman.

"Smoke," I replied sheepishly.

"Pardon?" the man said.

"Never mind," I replied.

REEL TO REAL

In the movie *Burnt*, a top chef allows poor decisions and a bad temper to sideline his career. After recovering from his abuse of drugs, the chef attempts to restart his culinary career by opening up a new restaurant. The dream arises slowly because the chef's past creates unforeseen obstacles along the way.

I made some bad choices in my first few years in the pulmonary field. I worked persistently with no breaks. I never took time for myself, and I rarely sought help from anyone. This was a pattern I had developed early on in my life. Working with difficult patients in a difficult field exacerbated the problem. Consequently, I burned out. It wasn't until I evaluated my previous decisions and took a long look at my career that I realized I needed to leave the profession, at least temporarily. Unfortunately, it took waiting in an unemployment line to come to this understanding. Only a fool continues down a path that knowingly leads to destruction. I had nothing left to give, and I negatively impacted others. Moving forward, I would have to find the right recipe to prevent burnout from occurring again if reentering the pulmonary field was to be part of my future.

SMOKE SCREEN TEST

Do you find yourself with less tolerance? Are you irritated by things that never irritated you before? Are you saying to yourself, "I can't take this anymore!" You may be on the verge of burning out. Seek help and apply management tools before your flame goes out.

Sometimes evaluating your situation is necessary to ensure you're in the right field.

CHAPTER 5

THERE'S SOMETHING ABOUT MARY

I SAT DOWN IN the employee break room and let out a sigh of disgust. I placed my head in my hands, took some deep breaths, and hoped that this brief period of silence would reenergize me. I attempted to enjoy the solitude. I was alone, but it wasn't quiet. There were noises in the room.

Every inanimate object communicated uniquely. The chair wanted to retire evidenced by the many tiny holes in its upholstery. It looked as if a shotgun had blasted it. Of the four wheels, only three touched the ground at any one time, posing a threat of seasickness to the sitter who moved too much. The wallpaper seemed to be falling asleep as it slowly unraveled from the ceiling to the floor. The fluorescent lights seemed ready to clock out as their darkened ends grew closer together. Even the faucet sought reprieve as it dripped continuously, once every second. With metronome-like regularity, it whispered, "Please - Re - Place - Me!"

This arbitrary group came together to form a choir lamenting with the same song. Each item sang its verse, while they all sang the same chorus: "We are tired."

What a pitiful scene, I thought. *Is this what my career had turned into—a struggle to maintain energy to make it through a day?*

I had academic degrees. I had experience. Now my entire job consisted of doing the same thing: pulling foul smelling, copious sputum out of people's lungs. How could I return to work each day? I arrived at the hospital each morning fresh, but by the end of the day, I questioned my career choice. I had burned out only a year before. What prevented me from burning out and quitting again? What was my secret to longevity?

Before I could discern an answer, my thoughts were interrupted. The vent alarmed in room six … again.

Prior to this moment, I had run non-stop. I treated one patient, then I treated another, and continued until I had seen all of my patients. Then I repeated the cycle. The monotony drained the life out of me. All the patients received the same treatment. They all had the same problems. They all faced the same outcome. Everyone had chronic diseases and resembled one another in condition and care. Nobody stood out, except one: room six.

Room six was a source of perpetual stress. I cringed at the thought of entering the room more than any other not because I disliked the patient nor because of the task. I disliked the room because it housed the one patient who reminded me of my failures. It took every ounce of motivation to care for the patient. The frustration could have driven me over the burned out ledge again had it not reminded me that I had developed one of the most essential tools I've ever used to manage burnout. And I was unaware I used it.

FAILING TO FIX

I prided myself on treating lung diseases. It is a large part of what I do. It's satisfying knowing I am an integral part in the therapeutic recipe for a patient. Seeing a patient transition from complete dependence on medicine to near independence is gratifying. But not all health can be returned. Sometimes diseases are permanent. Sometimes the damage cannot be reversed. In those cases, I rest in the understanding that at least I can provide support. If you can't breathe, we'll breathe for you is the unspoken motto. But room six was different. Room six held the patient whose health I could not restore. Nor, it seems, even support.

Room six was the temporary home of Mary, my pulmonary fibrosis patient. Mary arrived at our facility only a few weeks before, but she had made a lasting impact. Mary was petite and frail, weighing no more than 90 pounds. She was a mother and, as of a year ago, a grandmother. She was young, only in her mid-fifties, but she looked much older. The disease had taken its toll. It had riddled her body and made it weak and helpless. Pulmonary fibrosis caused her lungs to be chronically inflamed. It had progressed rapidly, forcing her lungs to lose their compliance or stretchiness. Her lungs had transformed from a flexible slinky to more of a car strut. She had received steroids, oxygen, and inhalers over the years, but nothing worked. Mary continued to decline. She could do nothing for herself. She couldn't even breathe without the help of the ventilator.

This really frustrated me. Her diseased progressed to the point that it had become almost impossible to support her with a ventilator. Despite all the advances in medicine and technology, despite all the training and experience I had, I could not ventilate Mary effectively. Her lungs were too stiff. When the vent tried to push air in, it struggled. Like a 2-cylinder car going uphill, it needed more power, specifically more pressure. But this required pressure limits. Too much force could rupture a lung. Therefore, I set pressure limits which, if reached, sounded an alarm. And alarm it did, almost continually.

The persistent alarm told me that Mary wasn't receiving the air she needed. As I entered the room, Mary communicated the same thing. But she didn't use words. Air didn't flow through her vocal cords to allow speech. The tracheostomy tube in her neck acted as a detour preventing any vibrations in her larynx (voice box).

Mary communicated other ways, primarily with her eyes. She had a look that spoke volumes. Mary always looked like she was on the verge of tears. Honestly, I think she was. Every time I entered the room, Mary looked at me with her heavy eyes weighed down by the thick, dark circles that permanently resided underneath. Although she couldn't speak, she could mouth words. Fortunately, I was fluent in lipreading thanks to the many opportunities for interpretation.

MARY'S WISH

Lipreading can be tricky, depending on the patient's articulation. Those that mumble or use a great deal of slang are more difficult to understand. I never had a problem understanding Mary for two reasons. First, she always spoke clearly and unmistakably, though without sound. I wondered if she had proper diction before she became ill. I could picture Mary teaching English class to students correcting them on their grammar, tone, and pronunciation. The second reason I never had a problem interpreting Mary's wishes was because Mary almost always said the same thing. Every time I entered her room, Mary repeated three simple words: Please - Help - Me.

Those words not only spurred every desire to be able to restore Mary's health but they also forced me to face my shortcomings. The more I tried to fix Mary, the more I failed. They say you only fail if you refuse to get back up when you're knocked down. That holds some merit, but there is a line where you know your efforts are futile. I thought I was approaching that line, but I kept trying.

I attempted relentlessly to help Mary. I changed settings on the ventilator, tweaked that knob, turned this dial, and tried various therapies. I analyzed her breathing pattern and assessed her condition meticulously to no avail. As soon as I made her comfortable, her breathing pattern changed. It always did.

Everyone's breathing pattern fluctuates. Typically, this irregularity is not a concern. Ventilators accommodate variations easily. In Mary's case, her disease made it difficult for the vent to detect subtle changes. Like a greyhound chasing a mechanical rabbit on a race track, the ventilator always seemed to be one step behind.

That's why I dreaded going into room six. I couldn't fix Mary. I knew she would ask me to help her, and I knew I would fail. I couldn't even support her, and every failed attempt only reminded me of that.

There was one alternative. It was always at the ready in situations like this, sedation. *If you can't inflate, sedate.* I preferred not asking for any sedation because it was only a temporary fix. Sedation just made the patient unconscious so the machine could completely take over. On the positive side, the patient ventilated. On the negative side, the patient was completely unaware of anything.

If the only way you can live is to be sedated entirely, is that living or just subsisting? Sedation does have its merits. It is essential and crucial during times of palliation. But Mary's situation was different. Although her disease was incurable, she was not likely to die tomorrow or next week. Mary had life left.

I chose not to ask for sedation. Mary requested help, and I wanted to provide that. What was different in this case was Mary's eyes. They asked for something more. Mary was tired. She needed rest, not just a reprieve from struggling to breathe.

KEVORKIAN SHMORKIAN

I decided to step outside the box. I grew tired of failing at my job, and I couldn't watch Mary struggle any longer. With a commitment to help my patient, I walked over to another therapist and asked her for a favor. "Will you hold my pager for a while?" I asked.

"Why?" the therapist asked.

"I'm going to turn off Mary's ventilator and stay with her," I replied.

"You're going to what!?" she fired back. "What do you mean you are going to turn off her vent?" Surprised by the sudden outburst, I paused for a moment before I realized the misunderstanding.

"Wait, I'm not going to let Mary die!" I responded, appalled by the thought of my co-worker. "I'm not Jack Kevorkian! I just want to allow Mary to sleep for a while." After allowing my colleague a brief sigh of relief, I handed over my pager. I walked into room six, sat down beside Mary's bed, and took out the bag-mask valve and breathed for Mary.

Ventilators are amazing pieces of technology, and they have advanced tremendously over the years. They can detect the slightest change in lung function and lung dynamics and make adjustments accordingly. Ventilators can notify you if there is a leak, and they can record information in real time. They are amazing inventions. But they are machines. There is no substitute for a good manual resuscitator when the situation warrants.

I placed the bag over Mary's airway. I observed what her body needed to ventilate. Once I determined her body's demands, I mimicked her breathing pattern. Within seconds, Mary fell asleep.

Mary slept for two hours. Two hours is both a short and a long time to watch someone sleep. The time appears brief unless you're squeezing a breathing device throughout the duration. Once Mary's breathing pattern stabilized, I developed a rhythm. The timing became reflexive. I watched television and daydreamed periodically.

Mary appeared peaceful. I switched hands to prevent cramping and rotated between sitting and standing to keep alert. Mary remained motionless except for the small rising of her chest during my manual inhalation. Occasionally someone would walk by the room and peer in expressing a confused look. Before they asked the question, I shook my head as if to say, "Not now." As a result, no one disturbed us.

When Mary finally awoke, she looked different. She appeared

rested. It was probably the best sleep she had had in months. It took Mary a moment to wake up, but when her eyes caught my eyes, she looked confused. She glanced at me and then looked at the clock. Her confusion turned to shock. "Have you been here the whole time?" she mouthed.

"Yes," I responded. "You said you wanted help, and you looked tired, so I let you sleep. Besides, I needed to catch up on some soap opera viewing. We both got what we wanted." Mary saw through my facetiousness, smiled, and thanked me repeatedly.

DEAR JIM

I wasn't scheduled to work for the next few days. I stayed busy during my time away running errands, cleaning my apartment, and exercising. In other words, nothing out of the ordinary.

When I returned to work, I heard the news. Mary had passed away while I was gone. The message surprised me. Mary was incredibly ill, but I thought she had several months left. I suppose her body couldn't take any more hardship. She was physically and emotionally exhausted, but now Mary finally had the rest she wanted.

Weeks passed, and Mary's name slowly faded from memory. A new patient occupied room six. After they discharged home, another patient arrived, and the cycle continued. The monotony of long-term care never ceases.

During one of the tedious workdays, the clinical director approached me and handed me an envelope. "This came for you," she said. I looked at the envelope that was addressed only to "Jim, RT." I went to the employee break room and silently greeted my weary companions: the crumbling chair, the sleepy lights, dripping faucet, and the gravity-stricken wallpaper. I opened the envelope and inside was a hand-written letter that started with "Dear Jim." Mary's daughter had written me a message.

Mary's daughter expressed how deeply appreciative she was that I had stayed with her mom that day. Mary had told her the story of how I squeezed the "breathing bag" for two hours, and her daughter recalled how much Mary smiled as she remembered the occasion. The visit turned into one of the best moments she ever had with her mom. Mary's daughter said she'd never forget how much that last moment meant to her.

I was speechless. I read the letter over and over again, and each time I became more emotional. I became lost in my thoughts. Letters like these are gold. They rarely surface, but when they do, they remind us that what we do matters. I had made a difference.

As I sat quietly in the break room, another vent alarm broke my concentration. I suddenly became aware of my surroundings again. The listless feelings returned. "How do I keep doing this?" I wondered. Suddenly, the answered dawned on me. Mary's letter reminded me that I had developed a tool to protect myself from burning out that I had completely forgotten about.

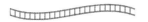

REEL TO REAL

There's Something About Mary is a film where Ted goes out of his way to reconnect with his high school prom date. He hires a private investigator, drives a thousand miles, and tries to rebuild a romance with Mary that has eluded him for twenty years.

For Ted, there was something about Mary that stayed with him. Ted's thoughts of Mary never left despite years of separation. For me, there was something about Mary in room six that did not stay with me. As I sat in the break room and reflected on the letter, I realized I never thought about Mary while I was away from work. I hadn't thought about work at all. I had never used a manual resuscitator for two hours on a patient before. That was not routine therapy. *Why had I not dwelled on this instance and talked about it with others during my time off?* I wondered.

The truth was, I had developed a habit that separated work from carrying over to home. After I burned out, I decided to leave the stresses of my job at work. When I removed my badge, I told myself work had finished. I did not dwell on difficulties of the day after I went home. Unbeknownst to me, this repeated behavior developed into a habit. My brain and body automatically went into recovery mode as soon as I removed my badge.

It wasn't until I read the letter from Mary's daughter that I realized I never thought of work at home. This separation allowed me to refuel at the end of each day and return to work rested, even if I was busy during my days off. I didn't burn out because I did not stay in a stressful state. What a revelation! I had developed an unconscious tool to manage burnout. As I folded up the letter I smiled and thought, *Thanks, Mary, I knew there was something about you.*

SMOKE SCREEN TEST

Are you taking the stress of work home? Are you increasingly thinking about the negative aspects of work when you're not there? When you daydream, are you thinking about work? Think about developing a habit or ritual that reminds you to separate work from home. Be conscious when you clock out, remove your scrubs/uniform, or when you close your car door. Tell yourself that work is now over. This small step can produce enormous benefit over time.

Developing proper habits decreases stress
and compounds into self-improvement.

CHAPTER 6

FLATLINERS

I'LL NEVER FORGET MY first day as a student during clinical rounds. As the seasoned therapist educated me on the finer points of pulmonary medicine, an emergency code paged overhead. The therapist paused and then directed me to follow her as we ran up flights of stairs to the scene of the emergency. Emergency codes in a hospital cause two opposite reactions within seconds of each other. For a split second, everything stops. People cease talking. Nobody moves. Everybody waits and listens for further details. A moment later, everybody jumps into action. Team members stop their previous tasks, gather necessary equipment, and quickly make their way to the scene.

Every situation is different, and every scenario is unique. Some situations are regrettable and others are unforgettable. Emergency codes provide the opportunity for many to showcase their skills and talents, or as it turned out in my case later in my career, expose a buildup of angst from past demons.

CAN YOU HEAR ME?

Rachel clocked in to work as she always did. Her day started at six o'clock in the morning and finished around four o'clock in the afternoon. If you're a morning person, it's a good schedule. She had spent the early part of her career as a bedside nurse but soon transitioned to working in Interventional Radiology (IR) performing routine outpatient procedures. She realized early on that she preferred working with less critical patients. Outpatient procedures consisted of prepping and assisting the placement of special catheters like Peripherally Inserted Central Catheters (PICC lines), placing Inferior Vena Cava (IVC) filters, and other specialized interventional radiology procedures. These procedures provided greater access to the body to administer medication and other difficult therapies.

It took a while to become competent in all the possible interventions but once you did, you were well respected. Rachel had this honor. She had earned her stripes, as it were, and had a wealth of experience behind her. Rachel could secure a catheter with stitches, cover it with the proper dressing, and clean up all the used equipment in seconds. If the patients were calves in a rodeo, she would be the tie-down roping queen of Radiology. Rachel enjoyed her work, in part because she always knew what to expect. She preferred the "business as usual" aspect of her job. Her patients were stable and predictable, at least so she thought.

I had become acquainted with Rachel over the years because my role required frequent visits to IR. When patients needed a special catheter, I would accompany them because they were either on a ventilator or had an artificial airway. In either case, they needed constant monitoring. Once I stabilized them in the IR, Rachel and her team took over. My brief experiences with Rachel assured me that she had everything under control in her area.

One particular morning started as a calm day. I savored these days. Nothing happened out of the ordinary. I saw my patients, gave them their necessary treatments, and attempted to get them one step closer to being discharged home. As I started to treat my last two patients, I heard the emergency overhead paging system. As usual, everything stopped. I froze in my tracks, listened intently, and waited to hear the location of the emergency. It was Radiology.

An emergency in Radiology is exceedingly rare. The population consists of non-critical and stable patients. Frankly, when an emergency page occurs for Radiology, it is usually a mistake. Sometimes someone accidentally hits the emergency button. Other times the operator announces the wrong location. Regardless, the validity of the emergency has to be verified, so I hurried down to Radiology to investigate. What I saw was bizarre.

As I entered the room, I saw Rachel on top of the procedure table ferociously pressing on a sea of blue material. *This is not a mistake*, I thought. *This is unusual.* If someone is already on the chest compressing the thoracic cavity to promote perfusion, then I immediately assess the airway. Is it patent? Is there an artificial airway in place? Is it secure? These questions were all those I ask during an assessment that takes only seconds to complete. However, in this instance, I could not see the patient's airway. In fact, I could not see the patient!

Practically every case in Interventional Radiology was officially a "sterile" procedure. To achieve this level of cleanliness, staff members cover the patient with an oversized blue drape to minimize

.....mination and the spreading of germs. I assumed there was a patient underneath this blue curtain, but one should never assume anything.

I immediately went to where the head of the patient should be while a nurse began taking notes to record the incident. When the patient's heart presumably stopped, the Radiology team attempted to push the sterile drape off of the patient's chest. However, the mountain of garb just piled up, mostly on the patient's face.

I started digging my way through the Himalayan attire like a dog trying to uncover his buried bone. When I finally reached the man's face, my jaw dropped. I couldn't believe what I saw. "Hold compressions," I told Rachel calmly.

Unfortunately, my recommendation fell on deaf ears. Rachel did not stop. She was a woman on a mission. Rachel looked visibly shaken. Her eyes were wide, and her face was red. Her adrenaline had kicked in and instinct had taken over. The first step in the event of a cardiac arrest is to start chest compressions. Rachel jumped on that step with full fervor.

You're not going to die here, she must have thought. *Not on my watch!* Rachel remained focused, unwavering in her pursuit to restart her patient's heart. Blood rushed to her face. She started to sweat. Her eyes fixated on the man's chest. She completely zoned out everything else, including my voice.

In Rachel's defense, chaos ruled the room, which happens occasionally. Every code is chaotic, but some are more controlled than others. During a code, the veterans remain calm and collected. For them, codes are routine. However, the novices and less experienced often react in less than stellar ways. Inevitably, codes bring out the control gene in many people resulting in a room full of captains and few, if any, crew. Too many people bark commands while few people listen because, changing analogies, there are too many chefs in the kitchen.

Realizing this reality, I raised my voice and repeated to Rachel, "Hold compressions." This time Rachel heard me, but surprisingly she still did not stop. She just looked at me as if to say, "You're not the doctor. You can't make that decision. I refuse to let this patient die!"

Am I invisible? I thought. *Are words resonating from my mouth? Maybe I only think my vocal cords are working. Perhaps I'm still asleep in bed, and this is just a ridiculous dream. Am I that insignificant that no one considers my opinion valid?"* This internal conversation had happened before. Being ignored was not a first time event, and this emergency aggravated a resentment that I had carried for years.

NURSERY RHYME TIME

One incident a year earlier epitomized my frustration. I was participating in multi-disciplinary rounds in the Intensive Care Unit to briefly discuss each patient's condition and direction of care. That was the plan. Having the input of several providers from various disciplines proved beneficial for patient care, provided every person participated. When asked, I would throw out my wisdom and give my input for each patient.

But during this day of rounds, my words rarely landed. They

drifted off in a sound-proof bubble never to be seen or heard again. With the first patient, the physician asked the group if anyone had anything to add about the patient's pulmonary status. Because I worked in the pulmonary field, I thought this would be a perfect time to participate. As I started to answer, he interrupted and then responded to his own question.

This happened again with the next patient. It was as if the physician asked the question because he felt obligated to follow a framework, not because he cared about the responses. When it came time to discuss the third patient, I decided to make a point. On cue, the physician asked if anyone had any information to add about this patient. Knowing the apparent irrelevant thoughts that would proceed from my mouth, I decided to experiment. I leaned over to a colleague and said, "Watch this." I cleared my throat and announced, "I have something to add." Then I proceeded to recite a well-known nursery rhyme. "Mary had a little lamb," I began. "Its fleece was white as snow. And everywhere that Mary went, the lamb was sure to go."

My colleague standing beside me couldn't believe what I said. She looked at me as if I were drunk or stupid or both. I'm sure she would have scorned my behavior had it not been for the reaction of the other nine members of the group. None of them acknowledged me. I spoke audibly. I annunciated and used animation for effect. No one else responded. Every other person turned and walked away toward the next location where we would discuss the care of the next patient on the list. There I stood, alone, reciting my nursery rhyme. It was as if I hadn't existed. My colleague shook her head.

"Does this happen often?" she asked.

"Unfortunately, it does," I replied. "It's so nice to be appreciated,"

I added facetiously. We both chuckled, and I thought I had dismissed the incident. The emergency code in IR reminded me that I had not.

CAN YOU HEAR ME NOW?

The code reminded me of all those times I've been ignored. I found myself becoming agitated. I thought about how important it was to remain calm during a code. I usually did. This time I noticed my anger erupting. When the sympathetic nervous system kicks in, many things happen to the body. The heart rate increases, airways dilate, and epinephrine/adrenaline is released in the body. It's the fight/flight response of the body. It's great for moments where you are in immediate danger. It's bad for incidents when you need to remain calm. For these moments, your body needs the parasympathetic nervous system. This is when heart rate slows, airways constrict back to normal, and everything relaxes. It's the rest/digest response of the body.

I knew I needed to calm down. I did not want my anger to take over. I began to breathe diaphragmatically. I took in slow, deep breaths to calm down and activate my parasympathetic nervous system. This tool is great in times of stress when you need to calm down. I continued breathing for a few more seconds until a doctor's voice interrupted me.

"Does anyone have a pulse?" he asked. I assumed he meant can anyone in the room palpate a pulse on the patient and not whether anyone in the room had a pulse. I would have loved to make a sarcastic remark highlighting this poor choice of words, but I thought under the circumstances it would not have been appropriate. Unfortunately, this question caused more chaos.

As soon as the physician asked the question, two or three people frantically searched for a pulse. They checked the arms, the groin, even the neck which was still partially occluded with the sterile drape. All the while Rachel pushed on the chest, full steam ahead.

During the search, I repeated my request to Rachel. *Maybe they will follow my recommendations this time*, I thought. "Hold compressions please," I said more sternly. To my astonishment, Rachel and every other chef in this dysfunctional kitchen continued their job as if auditioning for a spot on the next Iron Chef: Code Version.

HOW ABOUT NOW?

The code scene persisted for another couple of seconds until I looked at the patient again to verify what I noticed before. I saw the same thing which prompted me to react harshly. Sometimes, you have to force people to listen. It should be unnecessary to raise your voice, but circumstances occasionally warrant the outburst. In a perfect world, everyone's voice would be heard and respected. In a perfect world, all people would contribute to the betterment of society. Then again, in a perfect world, society would not need improvement, and there would be no hospitals anyway.

Thus, with built up frustration and a little bit of disgust, I grabbed Rachel's arm and yelled, "STOP!" Thankfully, everything halted. The doctor stopped searching for a pulse. The nurse ceased writing, and the ever dutiful Rachel finally held compressions. Everyone stared at me.

"Why have we stopped compressions?" the doctor asked incredulously. That was a great question. The RT does not run the code, the physician does. We are all teammates contributing to the patient's care, but someone has to be in charge. Someone has to lead. I gladly submit to another's authority, but sometimes the situation warrants speaking up and demanding an audience.

As everyone glared at me, I pulled back the sterile drape to reveal what had prompted me to tell Rachel to hold compressions initially. When I first dug through the piles of blue material that lay atop the patient's face, I noticed something unusual about the patient: he seemed to be wincing. Moreover, the scowl on his face grew more apparent with each consecutive compression. When I first noticed the grimace, I wanted Rachel to hold compressions to verify my observations. You can't genuinely grimace or scowl without a pulse. They are evidence of pain. Thus, if a patient reacts to pain with facial expressions, they probably do not need someone pushing their rib cage two inches below its normal resting position.

During my inner dialogue and frustration around being ignored, I noticed the winces increasing in severity. Finally, right before I shouted at Rachel, I looked at the patient and his eyes were open! Thus, the reason for my outburst.

The glares focused on me now shifted to the patient. I peeled back the blue drape revealing the patient's face to everyone else for the first time. I paused for a moment so everyone could understand why I howled as I did. Then, while gesturing to the patient, I answered the physician's question, "We always cease cardiac compressions when the patient says oww!"

REEL TO REAL

In the movie *Flatliners*, a group of medical students attempt to discover what lies beyond the boundary of death. Each member takes turns stopping their heart and going "flatline" for longer and longer periods. During their near death experiences, each member has various visions and experiences revolving around past demons.

As a Respiratory Therapist, I am often overlooked. Although I do not seek notoriety, I do wish to be heard. Being ignored connotes irrelevance and devalues a person. Admittedly, this is a source of frustration that I realized I hadn't resolved. The resentment is a personal demon I face, though I did not need to flatline to realize it. Thankfully, when a situation arises and irritability mounts, taking a moment to breathe diaphragmatically helps quell the stress. I can unleash the parasympathetic part of the nervous system and relax. Taking time for focused breathing works, and it's much safer than stopping my heart for a few minutes.

SMOKE SCREEN TEST

Are you noticing more tension in your neck or jaw? Has your libido dropped? Does it take more cups of coffee to wake you up in the morning? Do you crave salty foods? Are you experiencing more brain fog? These are all symptoms of adrenal depletion from stress. Stress can be physical, emotional, or psychological. Stress can be perceived or real. Breathing, meditating, and mindfulness can be beneficial for combating stress but make an appointment to see your physician too. There could be hormonal imbalances contributing as well.

Taking a moment to diaphragmatically breathe can alleviate the damage of stress to your body.

C H A P T E R   7

FLATLINERS—REVISITED

THE MAGIC NUMBER IS six. I have a maximum of six hours to complete my goal and no more. To quote Ed Harris's character, Gene Kranz, in the movie Apollo 13, "Failure is not an option." Timing is everything. When the patient enters the room, the clock ticks and the stress begins. De-stressing will have to occur later. Now, there is no time. Pressure builds and tensions climb as the recovery team anticipates the patient's arrival. Success depends on everyone working together. But success is not guaranteed. Some factors are outside our control. Everybody is on edge but ready. We know the patient will arrive at any moment.

It's quiet. The calm before the storm.

TIME: 1105

The operating room (OR) team pushes the bed into Surgical Intensive Care. I stand by ready to disconnect the patient from the OR's manual resuscitator to the vent. Multiple IV lines extend from the patient's neck and both of his arms, forming literal lifelines to portable poles. Plastic lines measuring only four millimeters in diameter are all that stand between existence and non-existence. They are, indeed, lines between life and death.

The transition is swift. The OR team provides a summation of the recent open heart surgery case, and the receiving ICU team absorbs the information like a sponge. Every teammate knows his and her role. All will work simultaneously and independently while forming a cohesive unit to ensure the patient remains stable and ready for the next phase of recovery. The time starts. We have six hours. It's 1105.

TIME: 1155

Mr. Ray looks lifeless. Days before he resembled the average middle-aged man. He spent years forming his oversized belly and accepted his new receding hairstyle. Prior to obtaining his routine physical, he had no indication anything was wrong. He had no difficulty breathing and experienced no chest pain. He felt short-winded when he exerted himself, but he chalked that feeling up to the common symptoms of aging. His electrocardiogram (EKG), which measures the electrical activity of the heart, revealed startling results. The report suggested Mr. Ray had had a previous heart attack. Mr. Ray recoiled at the notion. "How could I have had a heart attack without knowing it?" he asked.

Further tests would clarify. Other diagnostic tests confirmed the EKG. Mr. Ray had suffered a mild heart attack at some point in the recent past. More serious was the fact that the tests revealed another cardiac incident waiting to happen. Over ninety percent blockage on two arteries and seventy-five percent on another gave Mr. Ray an immediate ticket to the hospital. After another day of tests and preparation, Mr. Ray went in for surgery.

Today, residual Betadine, a skin antiseptic, stains his chest yellow. Just moments before, this chest was sawed open. Dr. Wolfson, the cardiothoracic surgeon, had cut through the sternum exposing the heart for the procedure. Dr. Wolfson performed three Coronary Artery Bypass Grafts (abbreviated CABG and affectionately referred to as a "cabbage times 3"). This procedure requires replacing significantly blocked arteries around the heart with non-occluded ones. The surgery creates a cardiovascular detour for blood-flow traffic.

Once Mr. Ray's vital signs stabilize, the OR team reverses the anesthetic agent. Sedation remains to mitigate pain while the tension of the task looms over our heads. The patient should breathe on his own as soon as possible. If we fail to accomplish our mission, a bevy of criticisms and discipline will rain down. I monitor any signs of spontaneous breathing. At first, there is nothing. Then I see it—a trigger symbol on the ventilator informing me that Mr. Ray is starting to wake up. I slowly adjust the settings to accommodate and watch carefully for any abnormal changes. Mr. Ray breathes a little on his own now, but he still needs help. Next phase completed. It's 1155.

TIME: 1310

Dr. Wolfson observes for a few minutes then leaves. He has another case to prepare. Dr. Wolfson is everything you want in a surgeon. He is meticulous, experienced, and thorough. His hair is thinning and mostly gray with some remaining black strands reminding observers of a time when his head was full of dark, thick hair. A shaded garden of hair covers his face while isolated patches of gray weeds force their way onto his manicured lawn of a beard. He has a youthful look but the touches of gray he sports in hair and beard assure everyone he has enough experience to be trusted.

The next hour begins uneventfully. Mr. Ray breathes more independently, and the nurse tapers his sedation. He progresses nicely but still needs support. Dr. Wolfson stops by before his next case to check Mr. Ray's status. "Time is ticking," he says. "Keep pushing him. Wean the vent. I would like him off in under two hours, but I'll settle for four." Everyone is well aware of the window: the six-hour period to wean the patient from the ventilator. Studies show patients do better without prolonged intubation (breathing tube) and mechanical ventilation. Patients without prolonged intubation also are able to leave the hospital sooner, saving the hospital thousands of dollars.

There are many drivers in the practice of medicine, and money always ranks near the pole position. "Aggressive but safe" is the understood motto. Push as much as you can without compromising care. Everyone is under pressure, including the patient. Thankfully, he looks stable. It's 1310.

79

TIME: 1330

Mr. Ray moves more. He turns his head from side to side, but he cannot lift his head off the pillow yet. Being able to lift his head is a sign that he is ready to extubate (have his breathing tube removed) and be taken off the vent. I assess his vital signs, listen to his lung sounds, and monitor his vent settings. I think another hour will be sufficient. The nurse agrees.

After a few years working with post-operative heart patients, it becomes easier to recognize the signs. Nothing left to do now but wait. It looks like we will have plenty of time to spare before our time limit is up. Dr. Wolfson and the patient will be pleased. It's 1330.

TIME: 1335

I start to gather equipment for the anticipated extubation. Removing the breathing tube from the patient is a celebrated time, especially for the patient. The patient can finally stop breathing through a straw, even one as large as eight and a half millimeters in diameter. Everyone looks forward to this moment. We begin to prepare when suddenly everything changes. It's 1335.

Without warning, all of Mr. Ray's alarms start screaming simultaneously. His respiratory rate reads zero. His volume says zero. His heart rate flashes red on the monitor continuously with one number, ZERO. "What in the world just happened?" I ask.

"I don't know," the RN responds. We check for a pulse, nothing. "Crap, call a code!" the RN yells so others outside the room can assist.

I jump on Mr. Ray's chest and begin compressions. A handful of other people arrive within seconds to assist. One takes control of Mr. Ray's breathing. Another gathers emergency medicine while another prepares to defibrillate the patient, if necessary. Though everyone rushes, everyone is calm. Veteran clinicians surround me. This event, though emergent, is commonplace and approached systematically and without panic. It is an honor to work with such professionals. It's still 1335.

TIME: 1336

"What happened?" asks the critical care physician covering the unit.

"He just went into cardiac arrest," explains the nurse. "We have no idea why." I continue to compress the chest, hoping I will not experience the one thing everyone hates to hear during a code.

All people are fragile. We pull muscles, sprain ankles, and pinch nerves seemingly at the drop of a hat. Sick people are even more vulnerable to injuries. But newly operated heart patients are incredibly delicate. Cardiopulmonary resuscitation (CPR) and the manual compression of someone's chest to perfuse vital organs are violent. Far from its television portrayal where the patient wakes up after a few seconds, breathes a sigh of relief, and verbally thanks everyone for saving his/her life before finishing the cup of ice cream that has not yet melted, CPR is graphic.

Brutal forces must accompany compressions for effectiveness. These forces often result in a common consequence of CPR that is never mentioned in cinema and causes all those within earshot to cringe simultaneously. As expected, that sound occurred. It's 1336.

TIME: 1336

After just sixty seconds of chest compressions, everyone's face recoiled at the sound. "Crack!" screamed Mr. Ray's chest. "Pop!" reverberated his ribs soon after. Those two noises emanating directly under my hands were the voices of Mr. Ray's cartilage and ribs succumbing to the pressure of the weight of my attempts to start his heart again.

For the heart to adequately pump blood to the body's organs, the resuscitator needs to compress the chest of the patient between two to two and a half inches. Moreover, personnel should perform this compression at a rate of one hundred to one hundred twenty times per minute. On a robust and intact thorax, this force can cause damage. On a feeble, healing chest, this force causes trauma. It's ugly. It's grisly. It's necessary. It's still 1336.

TIME: 1337

"Looks like he's in V-fib," claims one of the astute nurses. Ventricular fibrillation (V-fib) is like the heart seizing. It's a life-threatening cardiac arrhythmia where the heart quivers and does not pump blood to the body. The treatment is to send an electric shock to the heart, causing it to stop and hopefully reset itself with a normal rhythm.

"Let's shock at two hundred," orders the physician. A nurse charges the defibrillator to two hundred joules, and I continue compressions while another team member manually breathes for the patient.

"All clear, oxygen clear?" asks the nurse to ensure everyone has backed away from the patient to prevent shocking ourselves. I stop compressions and take a step back with the rest of the team members.

"All clear," everyone responds. The machine delivers the shock. Immediately, Mr. Ray's body responds, jerking violently and raising almost entirely off the bed. He almost becomes airborne for a split second as if he, well, had two hundred joules of electricity suddenly enter his body! Then something amazing happens. It's still 1337.

TIME: 1337

Before I can resume chest compression, the cardiac rhythm on the monitor changes. It looks like a normal sinus rhythm. At least three people, myself included, feel for a pulse.

"I have a good, strong pulse," I state, somewhat surprised.

"Me too," says one of the nurses, equally taken aback. Everyone's eyes fixate on the monitor then quickly turn back to the patient. After a brief moment, all eyes focus again on the monitor. Everything looks good. Mr. Ray has a normal sinus heart rhythm, and his blood pressure is almost normal. I place the patient back on the vent, and we all wait for another minute to ensure Mr. Ray remains stable. It's still 1337.

TIME: 1338

Mr. Ray continues to show no adverse effects from CPR, and his vital signs return to baseline. We decide to wait a while before resuming aggressive weaning. We are unsure how Mr. Ray will react. Though he remained sedated throughout the whole episode, the human body is a complex system. Each patient is unique. It's better to wait and see how Mr. Ray will respond. The physician orders lab work to search for any culprits. The occurrence is a setback, but we are still within the window. Plenty of time remains, but we did lose precious moments. Stress mounts. Back to the waiting game we go. It's 1338.

TIME: 1410

Mr. Ray remains stable. There are no signs of any residual effects from the code. It's agreed. We will resume aggressive weaning. I change the vent settings. The nurse adjusts the sedation. All vital signs remain stable. Onward we go, full steam ahead. We pass the three-hour mark. There is one more hour left to meet the surgeon's ideal goal but three more hours left before the window closes. This case will be close. It's 1410.

TIME: 1505

Four hours have passed since Mr. Ray arrived in ICU. He is doing very well, despite the brief cardiac episode. His sedation is off. He opens his eyes periodically, and he follows simple commands. He breathes entirely on his own, but he does have brief periods of apnea, moments of no breathing. I would love to extubate Mr. Ray, but I fear his sedation is still not entirely out of his system.

"I don't think he's quite ready," the nurse claims.

"I agree," I say. "Mr. Ray just needs a little more time." We both take another look at Mr. Ray and the monitor and give each other a look of agreement. As I begin to leave the room, Dr. Wolfson enters. He just finished his second case and decided to look in on Mr. Ray.

"He's still on the ventilator?" Dr. Wolfson asks rhetorically and with some aggravation.

"Yes," the nurse responds. "We had a brief setback when Mr. Ray went into V-fib and required a round of CPR and one defibrillation."

"When was this?" Dr. Wolfson asks, surprised and concerned.

"About an hour and a half ago," the nurse responds. "Since then he has been stable. He is progressing nicely, but we feel he's not quite ready. He is still too lethargic."

"Fair enough," Dr. Wolfson says. "Has he had any other abnormalities since then?"

"No, just the one," the nurse replies.

"Okay, keep at it," Dr. Wolfson says as he leaves the room. It's always reassuring to see a surgeon check on his patients after surgery. After the ICU team receives the patient, the responsibility of patient care falls mainly on the Critical Care Physician. But all the team members stay involved. Two hours remain. It's 1505.

TIME: 1620

Less than one hour remains before the six-hour time-limit window closes. Nobody wants to have to explain why a postoperative patient failed to come off the ventilator. If anyone had an excuse, we did. Mr. Ray went into cardiac arrest. His heart stopped beating, after all. If anyone deserves some latitude, it's Mr. Ray.

Mr. Ray looks good. He has no signs of apnea. He follows commands and his vital signs are stable. One more criterion to meet.

"Mr. Ray, do you want the tube out of your throat?" I ask facetiously. Mr. Ray nods affirmatively. In twenty years of medicine, I have never had a patient reply in the negative to such a question.

"Okay," I respond. "Then lift your head off the pillow." Slowly, Mr. Ray raises his head just a few inches away from the pillow. It is difficult, but Mr. Ray succeeds. "Fantastic!" I respond. "Mr. Ray's ready," I tell the nurse. "Are you okay for me to pull the tube?"

"Yes, go ahead," the nurse replies.

As I gather all the equipment for the second time, I reflect on Mr. Ray's journey from surgery to cardiac arrest to cracking ribs and now to this moment. The irony is that Mr. Ray will have no memory of the operation or cardiac arrest. That is a relief. I also reflect on the concept of time. Time can cause stress, as in a surgical situation, or it can be the source of relaxation, as in sitting on a beach enjoying a sunset. It all depends on the context. I knew the more stress time caused, the more time I needed to de-stress. It was ironic.

I deflate the cuff surrounding the endotracheal tube. Air rushes around the tube and out of Mr. Ray's mouth for the first time in hours. It's a pleasant sound indicating a patent or open airway, but it is not a pleasant odor. Imagine morning breath combined with the smell of plastic and sputum. It's not the fragrance you yearn to have emanating from your diffuser! I unfasten the tube holder and disconnect the tube from the ventilator.

"Take a deep breath in, Mr. Ray," I say. Then in one fail swoop, the tube is out. Mr. Ray smiles and nods his head out of gratitude. The time-limit window closes, but we closed it. We extubated within six hours, and, more importantly, Mr. Ray rests comfortably. Everything looks good. Dr. Wolfson will be pleased. Last piece of this recovery phase complete. It's 1620.

THE WINDOW IS STILL OPEN

A few days pass before I return to work. The time off has revived me. Today's caseload does not require me to work in the ICU. As I walk around the recovery unit, I pass a room whose occupant catches my eye. "Mr. Ray?" I ask.

"Yes, sir," Mr. Ray responds, extending his hand out of politeness.

"How do you feel today?" I ask.

"Good. I feel good," Mr. Ray says, not knowing who I am.

"You probably don't remember me, but my name is Jim," I say. "I am the one who pulled out your breathing tube a few days ago."

"Oh, okay," Mr. Ray says, vaguely remembering the moment.

"I wanted to check on you and see how your chest feels," I say somewhat concerned about the response I will get.

"It feels good," Mr. Ray answers, "though it is a little sore."

"Yeah, about that," I say, slightly lowering my head. "Your heart decided to go on strike for a moment and stop beating while you were in the ICU. I had to push on your chest to convince it to start again. One of your ribs rebelled and voiced its opposition by popping. Sorry about that." Before Mr. Ray could respond, a voice chimed in from behind me.

"Oh, no, that is completely all right," says Sophia, Mr. Ray's wife as she rose from a chair I hadn't seen. "We are very grateful. Aren't we, honey?" Sophia asks while looking at her husband.

"Oh, absolutely!" Mr. Ray responds with complete agreement. "Thank you so much!"

"Well, don't let it happen again," I say jokingly. "You almost broke our window."

"Window?" Mr. Ray asks confused.

"It's a long story," I respond.

REEL TO REAL

In the movie *Flatliners*, a group of medical students attempt to discover what lies beyond the boundary of death. Each member takes turns stopping their heart and going "flatline" for longer and longer periods of time. The first student stays flatline for one minute. The next wants to go thirty seconds longer. The next students wants to go even longer. All of the students know time is critical and the longer they stay flatline, the less chance of recovery.

Time can be looked at in different ways. It can feel slow during an arduous workday, and it can seem fast on a good one. It can also be a source of stress when it is used as the measurement between a successful surgery or a poor one.

For every minute I am in a stressful moment, I find I need another in a non-stressful situation. Some refer to this as work-life balance, but that is only accurate if one is stressful and one is not. Sometimes work and life are both stressful. Thankfully, my home life at the time was free of stress.

When at home, I take advantage of the time to enjoy things that relax me. I always make a point to find something that makes me laugh. Whether it be a movie, book, or spending time with someone I know will bring out humor, I am intentional about laughing. I also enjoy exercising and learning new things. All of these things provide the necessary refueling needed to deal with the stresses of the workplace. Also, on my days off I don't wear a watch. There is no six hour window for me to monitor. Time is neutral, how I use it is not.

SMOKE SCREEN TEST

What is important to you? What is a non-negotiable? What words would others use to describe you? These are all ways to discover your values. Applying this knowledge helps with decisions and makes the best use of your time. For example, if you value organization, then look for ways to implement this at work or home. If you don't use your values, then you will be on a one-way path to burning out.

Taking time to rest, relax, and separate yourself
from stress quells burnout.

C H A P T E R   8

REAR WINDOW

I LOATHE YELLING, ESPECIALLY if I am the object. Who doesn't? For some, yelling motivates action. Sport coaches often shout at their players to enhance performance. Drill sergeants are notorious screamers causing soldiers to jump to attention, and parents sometimes howl at their children because They - Will - Not - Listen! But yelling has always had the opposite effect on me. When someone barks at me, I am not inspired. I am not swayed. I tend to shut down and become distant, and I usually ignore the culprit until he or she calms down.

Thankfully, I rarely witness such behavior. In over two decades of working in the medical field, I have only had to bear the brunt of someone's vociferous diatribe once. I recall the one moment when someone, seemingly out of nowhere, screamed and ranted at me for sixty full seconds for something I thought was utterly innocuous. The incident briefly paralyzed me. Thoughts of quitting, leaving the profession, and a myriad of burnout feelings emerged as a result. It was from the unlikeliest of sources I found guidance.

91

THE CALM BEFORE THE STORM

Dr. Jefferies was particular about everything. The first clue was how he dressed. He cared about his appearance. Dr. Jefferies groomed his hair precisely and always appeared at work clean shaven. He also had impeccable taste in clothes. Dr. Jefferies dressed in a neatly pressed suit and tie every day and wore shoes shiny enough to see his reflection. When seeing patients, he completed his ensemble by donning a white lab coat, making his medical presence unmistakably known. Dr. Jefferies would be the cover model of *Physician Quarterly* if there were such a periodical. He was also very meticulous. Dr. Jefferies wanted everything in its place at the right time and in the right way. Though quirky, he had every quality you desired in a doctor: expertise, skill, and confidence.

I rarely encountered Dr. Jefferies because our fields seldom coincided. He was a Gastroenterologist, and I worked in pulmonary. But on occasion, our disciplines crossed. The most memorable moment involved Mr. Doyle, a patient we shared. Mr. Doyle had severe lung disease and depended on the ventilator to breathe. He received nutrition and tube feedings through a nasal gastric tube inserted through his nose.

Because his condition was chronic, the attending physician decided Mr. Doyle needed a percutaneous endoscopic gastrostomy (PEG) tube for long-term feeding. The PEG tube was a tube inserted in the stomach where liquid nutrition could be given. Mr. Doyle's ability to feed orally would not return anytime soon, if ever, so a PEG tube was a reasonable alternative. Dr. Jefferies was called in to consult. After assessing Mr. Doyle, Dr. Jefferies agreed to perform the PEG placement in the Endoscopy Procedure room.

Also, Dr. Jefferies suggested performing a colonoscopy as Mr. Doyle had had chronic constipation for weeks, most likely from the various opioids and pain medication that had been given to Mr. Doyle throughout his stay. Consequently, I needed to accompany Mr. Doyle throughout his procedure to manage his vent and ensure his airway remained patent.

When the procedure time arrived, the nurse and I transported Mr. Doyle to the endoscopy room. The room was dark. Overhead recessed lights barely lit the room giving it a calm, welcoming atmosphere. A sink and a few cabinets were the only stationary objects in the room. A monitor, portable tables, and an array of other medical equipment littered the area covering up bland, earth-colored wallpaper that was decades past its expiration date. I set up the vent, and the nurse secured the IVs, leaving less room in an already crowded workspace. At this point, I usually stood back, watched the patient, and ensured everything remained stable. But today was different.

Increasingly, over the past several years, staff coverage had been cut. Administration persistently downsized staff to keep in the black and maintain profitability (or "revenueability" for the non-profit organizations). No healthcare discipline is immune. This day, the shortage manifested itself in the endoscopy room. Usually, there are two endoscopy personnel to assist the physician. This day there was only one.

Lisa was the endoscopy assistant preparing the equipment. I noticed her flushed face even under the dark lighting. Lisa was stressed. She hurried around preparing the equipment like a squirrel gathering nuts before winter. She was trying desperately to ensure everything was ready and in its place on time. With help, this job would have been routine. But Lisa was alone, and she was preparing to assist Dr. Jefferies. I could only imagine how precise he required everything to be, and she did her dutiful best to accommodate.

"Do you need any help?" I asked.

"Not right now," Lisa replied, "but during the procedure, we may need you to hand us a few things. I'll let you know."

"Sure, just tell me what to do," I responded. Sometimes trying to help someone who has a routine and knows precisely what they're doing causes more harm than good. You end up just getting in the way. So, I stood back and waited for any instructions.

Several minutes elapsed. Thankfully, Dr. Jefferies was a little late. The delay gave Lisa enough time to finish her preparation. She exhaled a sigh of relief as her flushed face returned to its normal color. The room was quiet now. There was no more shuffling, no more moving tables, and no more clanging of equipment on the metal tray. The only sound was the quiet hum of the ventilator fulfilling its obligation as life support.

Everything was in its proper place. Syringes lined up on the tray in military precision. Medicines rested in order of their intended use. Equipment waited in silent anticipation. The order of everything felt soothing, like sitting on the bank of a calm lake early in the morning. Lisa and I waited. A few more minutes passed before Dr. Jefferies entered. He drifted in the procedure room quietly like morning fog over this peaceful lake. He had an air of confidence. He held his head high and his chest out. This was his room. This was his procedure.

Dr. Jefferies paused briefly as if to verify everything was in order. He was not disappointed. Lisa had perfected her preparation. She could have performed it blindfolded. Dr. Jefferies positioned the patient to lie slightly on his right side. He took the endoscope and lowered it down Mr. Doyle's esophagus. He took a quick look at the interior of the stomach. Everything looked good. Dr. Jefferies poked the outside of the stomach as he watched the monitor for the corresponding interior effect. He grabbed a marker and drew the letter "X" to mark the spot where he would make the incision. *Please don't say X marks the spot*, I thought. That cliché would make even Mr. Doyle's sedated eyes roll. Thankfully, Dr. Jefferies said nothing. He continued the procedure with the utmost precision. It was apparent he had performed this procedure a thousand times. His technique was flawless.

THE TSUNAMI OF WORDS

The time came for Dr. Jefferies to place the PEG tube in the lining of Mr. Doyle's stomach. Dr. Jefferies carefully opened the box with the PEG tube inside and discarded any unnecessary pieces. He tilted his head slightly to his left and with a voice barely above a whisper and asked Lisa for Chlorhexidine, the antiseptic he would use to cleanse Mr. Doyle's skin. But Lisa had her hands full. Without verbalizing, Lisa looked at me and pointed with her eyes by raising her eyebrows and looking at the box of Chlorhexidine on the edge of the tray. I recognized my cue immediately. I took the box, opened it, and handed the medication to Dr. Jefferies without saying a word. It felt inappropriate to disturb the tranquil ambiance that enveloped the room. Suddenly, the atmosphere drastically changed. What was once a serene waterfront procedure room suddenly turned into a tsunami of chaos.

"What are you doing?" screamed Dr. Jefferies.

"What?" I replied in complete astonishment from the verbal storm that seemingly came out of nowhere.

"Now I need a new box of antiseptic!" Dr. Jefferies yelled, this time at a much higher decibel.

"Uh, what?" I said as I tried to decipher the rationale for such an outburst. I was baffled. I couldn't understand why Dr. Jefferies was upset. He wanted the Chlorhexidine, and I gave him Chlorhexidine. I didn't give him the wrong medication. I didn't throw the medication. Nor did I make any sarcastic or snide remark, which was an amazing show of restraint considering the abundance of comedic fruit that hung on the tree just waiting to be plucked. I could have made any number of comments about "butt" cams, being at the "wrong end" of things, get his thoughts on the government's "Fanny" Mae debacle, or discuss his opinion on "anal" retentive people.

However, I controlled myself. I was a professional. I didn't say anything. I just stared. I didn't shut down or ignore Dr. Jefferies. To my surprise, I just froze. Maybe it was from the shock of the contrast in moods. I don't know. After a moment, I looked at Dr. Jefferies with my head slightly tilted like a confused dog trying to comprehend the English language. *What a transformation*, I thought. *Is this how Dr. Jefferies is all the time?* I wondered. *I wore gloves. I didn't open the medication. What would have happened had I sneezed? Dr. Jefferies probably would have had a massive stroke, seized uncontrollably, collapsed, then floated away from a gust of "derriAIR.*

Exasperated at my apparent ineptness, Dr. Jefferies finally shouted the rationale for his actions. "You touched the medicine! Now it's not sterile!" After this, Dr. Jefferies let his deluge of anger fly. For the next sixty seconds, wave after wave of vitriol spewed from his mouth about germs, infections, and the importance of doing things right. I was shocked that the only apparent reason for the outrage was that I wasn't wearing *sterile* gloves. All I could think about was the notion of sterility. Technically, the medication lost any possibility of sterility as soon as it came in contact with the air. Moreover, the next place the tube was going was in the mouth of Mr. Doyle. Now that's not sterile! Then I thought about how ridiculous this situation was. *Why should I tolerate such behavior?* Waves of thoughts surfaced. *Maybe, it's time for me to leave this job. Could I find another profession?"* But I had no conceivable alternative. I wouldn't know where to begin. All I knew was I couldn't take much more of this outburst.

Finally, after Dr. Jefferies' raging storm ended, I replied to my apparent gross incompetence with only one word, "Okay." With that, Lisa obtained another box of antiseptic that she handed to Dr. Jefferies with perfect technique. I stood back and tended to my verbal lumps. I had made a mistake, but I thought the reaction was completely unnecessary. I thought about how best to respond and concluded that I would let the matter drop. I assumed Dr. Jefferies had the patient's best interest in mind. Mr. Doyle's health and care were Dr. Jefferies top priority, and I respected that. But the event left its mark.

Dr. Jefferies finished the PEG placement with no more debacles from me. However, Mr. Doyle needed a colonoscopy which meant the intervention had to continue. We shifted the focus from the anterior to the posterior. A different "end" required different equipment, especially a different scope. Lisa, as expected, had everything ready. I moved to the front side of Mr. Doyle so Dr. Jefferies could focus on Mr. Doyle's "backside." There was nothing for me to do except monitor Mr. Doyle.

As I watched the waveforms on the ventilator and monitored for any signs of discomfort from Mr. Doyle, I reflected on the verbal storm that occurred just a few minutes ago. I couldn't imagine this was the first time Dr. Jefferies had reacted this way. Surely, others have had the unfortunate experience of hearing such a tantrum. Why hadn't they said anything? I considered myself as having thick skin when it comes to people's behavior, but even I was taken aback. It was very disruptive. Though I had decided to let the matter drop, I continued to consider if this job was worth it. I thought, *Am I just upset over the behavior, or is this more evidence that I should move on?*

I questioned my role and value, and the only answer I found was that I didn't have the answer. I needed another's input.

MR. DOYLE'S OUTPUT

I considered whom I could ask for advice until something happened that completely changed my outlook on the entire situation. As Dr. Jefferies was at the "tail" end of his colonoscopy, a faint buzz came from Mr. Doyle. This sound caused me to turn my head and look toward Dr. Jefferies just as he bent over to get a closer look to see what was "behind" the vibrations. Suddenly, as Dr. Jefferies examined the "seat" of noise, a cacophony of notes blasted out of Mr. Doyle's rear!

Everything that followed seemed to be in slow motion. The violent eruption caused Dr. Jefferies' head to snap back from the shockwave. His hair blew back from the force of the blast as if Dr. Jefferies had suddenly put his head out of the window of a speeding vehicle. The New York Philharmonic could not have produced a sound as harmonious as this. And the timing couldn't have been more perfect! A second earlier or later would not have produced the same effect.

It was all I could do not to scream with happiness and laugh uncontrollably. I looked at Lisa to have someone to share this moment with, and I could see a buildup of water under her eyes. I never saw such joy in another's face. If she could, she would have run out of there singing a song of praise.

Of all the people and all the situations, no one was more deserving at this moment to receive this symphony of gas in the face than Dr. Jefferies. Flatulence never sounded so sweet.

Mr. Doyle had spoken. Though he was unconscious and sedated, he had announced to Dr. Jefferies that his outburst was inappropriate and there were consequences for such actions. I could not add anything. I had this moment as my retribution. No amount of verbal scolding or punishment from Dr. Jefferies' superior would ever top Mr. Doyle's statement on the issue. As far as I was concerned, the situation was over because there couldn't be a better "ending."

But I still needed help thinking through my career choice. I decided that the best place to turn was someone completely detached from the situation. I sought help from a life coach.

Without giving advice or dictating a course of action, the coach help me think through alternatives and goal setting. The process allowed me to look at my situation from a different angle and, to add one more pun to an already saturated story, to focus on the "end" goal.

REEL TO REAL

Following an accident, wheelchair-restricted Jeff spends his time observing his neighbors from his apartment window in the thriller *Rear Window*. After becoming convinced that one of his neighbors has committed a crime, Jeff seeks help from his nurse and girlfriend to gather evidence for his case. As the story unfolds, Jeff watches helplessly as lives are in danger.

Feeling helpless paralyzes actions. Over the years, I felt stuck in my job at times with no realistic option for change. Like Jeff in the movie, I had to seek help from others. Though Mr. Doyle's response to Dr. Jefferies' outburst was priceless, I still needed assistance to consider whether I should pursue other career options. It was on the suggestion of a former professor that I sought help from a life coach.

Over the next few months, the life coach did not counsel or consult but helped me realize where I was and where I wanted to be. The coach guided my thoughts and helped me discern the best steps to get to my destination.

Ultimately, I decided to stay in the medical field. Being yelled at by Dr. Jefferies made me feel immobilized with no alternatives, though that proved to be incorrect. Seeking help not only allowed me to see things from different perspectives, it provided another resource to stifle burnout.

SMOKE SCREEN TEST

If your future self could write a letter to your present self what would the letter say? When was the last time someone really listened to you? Do you know what you would like to do in five years? Do you know how to accomplish it? Seeking assistance from a qualified coach can help keep burnout at bay.

Asking for help is important to decrease burnout and assist in life's direction.

CHAPTER 9

SARAH'S KEY

I SAT ALONE BEHIND a desk. Darkness engulfed the room except for one light illuminating the phone in my hand. I froze. I couldn't do it. I couldn't make a simple phone call. I've made hundreds of thousands of phone calls in my life, but this one was different. This phone call brought anxiety and tension. The apprehension told me I wasn't ready to pick up the phone. But I had no choice. The idea that the conversation would be with my parents eased the concern. They would understand. All I needed to do was press the numbers on the keypad. I needed to stop thinking and move forward.

"Hey, Mom, Dad," I said. "… I'm okay … how are you?"

I sighed after I said okay. It was the lungs' way of announcing, *he's lying*. But I couldn't just vomit my story immediately. I wasn't there yet, in that place. I didn't even know if I could get there. I needed something, something from them. I needed permission. But how could my parents give me permission for something they didn't know I needed permission for?

"Yes, I did work today," I responded. "Uh, no, no it wasn't."

There it was. A simple question inviting me to participate and so soon in the conversation. But before I could begin sharing my story, strange things started to occur. My vision blurred. Fluid flowed from my eyes. My lower lip had what can only be described as a minor seizure, and everything on the inside of my nose suddenly wanted to be on the outside. I couldn't believe I was losing control. But this could be good. I should go with it. I need to keep my poise and not drop my head. I need to welcome silence. I need to stay in the moment.

"I lost a patient today," I explained solemnly.

"Lost," what an odd euphemism! My patients can't breathe let alone wander away and vanish. But what other word could I use? Kill? What an absurd notion. But "lost" was pregnant with significance. How could my parents understand the gravity of what happened unless they knew the backstory? How do I explain that the nurse called me and told me that the family in room fourteen was ready to extubate? First, I would have to explain that "extubate" meant "pulling the plug." Second, I would have to explain that "pulling the plug" is a misnomer because there is no *actual* plug.

"I had to disconnect someone from the ventilator," I continued.

That's two this week. I couldn't believe I lost *another* patient. As a Respiratory Therapist working in the Intensive Care Unit, I knew this was part of my job. I am the one responsible for the patient's breathing. I am the one who uses machines to assist failing patients. I am the one, not the doctor or the nurse, who removes the patient from those machines if the situation warrants.

"She was such a sweet lady," I explained. "You would have enjoyed her, Mom, because she looked like your mother. Her name was Elsie. She was barely five feet tall with short, white hair. Her hair blended in with the bed linen so well you couldn't tell where her hair stopped and the pillow case started. When she was awake, she was always thanking me for everything by nodding or patting me on the hand as a gesture of gratitude. I wish all of my patients were like her."

Unexpectedly, my words flowed effortlessly. I was reliving the moment. I could see Elsie. I could see the room, the bed, and all the machines surrounding her like soldiers protecting a fallen comrade. It felt like I was there.

"She was special," I continued. "Initially, I was frustrated because no one asked the family to leave the room while I prepared the patient."

"Prepare," what another strange euphemism! In truth, I didn't prepare the patient. I prepared the family. I prepared them to grieve and to say goodbye one last time.

"So, I had to do it," I said. "When I walked into the room, the family had their heads bowed out of respect, except for one son. He looked angry."

I'll never forget him. The son fixed his glare on me as if to say, *I'll always remember you as the one who killed my mother.* He didn't understand there was nothing else to do. He didn't realize that preparing a patient was hard to watch. Things happen to the human body when it dies that are difficult to see. These images are not the final ones you want to have of your loved one. Besides, this was my time, and I had a routine. I followed a slow, deliberate process, almost ritualistic. The process gave me my time to say goodbye.

I wanted to share my technique with my parents, but it felt too personal, too private for some reason. Each ventilator withdrawal brings unique challenges, but they usually start out the same way. Stillness envelops the room interrupted only by the sound of equipment removed: the slight tear of the Velcro that holds the breathing tube in place, the guttural air leak from the mouth after deflating the cuff that seals the tube in the airway, and the final sound of the vent being switched off. It was as if each piece of equipment bid their solemn farewell.

I wanted to tell my parents that for Elsie, I placed my hand on her head, stroked her hair one last time, and said my silent prayer of comfort for her and her family. But I couldn't. I was emotionally exhausted. I just wanted the call to end. The conversation dragged on. How much longer must I relive this moment? If the call doesn't stop soon, I may lose it. Finally, I heard it. Two words that brought instant relief.

"And ... scene!" the instructor said. "Great acting choice, Jim, very believable."

What a relief! The end of a beginner's acting exercise where I had to relive a vulnerable moment from my past. I had performed well. I stayed in the moment. But something strange happened that I hadn't expected. Everything about the scene was accurate: the situation, the patient, the environment, and even the phone call. Everything happened, except for the emotions. My original call to my parents produced no emotions.

What was it about being on stage that caused this to happen? Good actors have the ability to express the needs of a created character. But in this exercise, I was the character. What needs did I have? I didn't need to create a backstory. I needed no writer's imagination. I just had to relive a past moment. Why did I become so emotional during the exercise? What changed? Was I that good of an actor?

SEARCHING FOR KEYS

When I returned to work later that week, an image appeared to me as I continued to think about the acting exercise. The image was of a large, ornate mansion with Corinthian columns and hundreds of rooms. Each room had a door. Some of the doors were open revealing a clean, tidy room. The beds made, the towels folded, and the drapes neatly pressed and opened to reveal a picturesque outdoor view. Everything about the rooms was in order. But there were also many rooms with shut doors. Your curious side wanted to peer inside, but the fearful side hesitated. If you summoned enough courage to turn the doorknob, you realized it was locked. The only way inside was with a key. But you didn't know where the keys were, and you didn't have enough time to look for them. Life was too busy.

"Jim, we need you in room thirty for a possible vent withdraw," the nurse stated.

Are they kidding me? I just finished reliving a similar scene on stage! Now I need to "prepare" to "lose" yet another patient!

"Also, the daughter of the patient wants to speak with you before you do anything," the nurse continued. "She's waiting for you in the conference room."

That was strange. I've talked with many family members *after* withdrawing their loved from the ventilator, but no one ever requested to speak to me *before* I did anything. And why me? I was intrigued.

I went to the conference room. I slowly opened the door and glanced inside. Sarah was sitting motionless behind the table. She was not what I expected. Sarah was stoic and calm. She had perfectly straight auburn hair that extended to her shoulders. Her blouse and pants were neatly pressed and free of any noticeable wrinkles. Her flawless posture resembled a character of Victorian nobility. It completed a persona that said, *I am organized. I am in control.* In front of her rested a blank notepad and pen, meticulously placed. She showed no signs of emotions, and her manner was matter of fact as she spoke about the decision she was about to make.

"I want to discuss the care of my father with you," Sarah said curtly. "A short time ago I met with my pastor, and he informed me that in addition to your position here, you work with him and other staff members at church. Since I was unsure how this process works, the pastor recommended I talk with you to clarify some of the steps." No one had asked me to discuss details of withdrawing before. How unusual. Maybe this was Sarah's way of coping with the situation. Maybe by understanding the process, she would get a sense of closure that possibly had eluded her up to this point.

I explained the step-by-step procedure as clearly as I could, but it seemed so technical and apathetic. I wondered if Sarah was even listening. Suddenly, I noticed something different about Sarah. Her demeanor changed. Her once stoic face subtly revealed some emotions. Her eyes filled up with tears, and her posture relaxed. Though she still held her pen, she no longer took notes. She just stared off into the distance. Perhaps Sarah was coming to grips with the situation and could finally obtain some closure.

Then, just as suddenly, everything reversed. Sarah quickly regained her composure. She wiped away her tears and sat up straight. It was as if expressing emotions somehow signified losing control.

"I just need to know my role in all of this," Sarah said. "What am I supposed to do?" Role? I must not have been clear. Sarah had no role. She didn't have to do anything. Her father's lung disease was at the end stage. The vent merely prolonged the inevitable. If she agreed to move forward and withdraw, then her role ended.

"You don't need to do anything," I said. "Just be with your father." I expected to see some relief from that statement, but the comment only brought silence. Sarah didn't respond. She sat there, motionless. The silence became a little awkward. I didn't know what she was thinking, but somehow, I knew I shouldn't speak first. Sarah needed to break the silence. And she finally did.

"Howard took care of everything," Sarah mumbled.

"Your father?" I asked.

"Yes," she answered. "He took care of the finances, my mom, the house, everything. When Mom passed away, he started a Bible study group so he could care for them. He led the discussions, visited people when they were sick, and even helped others with their finances. He was a constant servant. That's the responsible thing to do, he would say. Sarah, always be responsible. Serve others. Don't let them down.

I could visualize Howard saying and doing these things. He was a towering man, very conspicuous. I never saw him stand up, but he must have been an intimidating figure. His hands could cover my whole head, and his feet were the size of scuba fins. When he spoke, I'm certain people listened. It was ironic. It's usually the giants among us who are the most gentle.

"But he never wanted to be maintained on the ventilator," Sarah said more emphatically. "He told me so. He had battled lung disease long enough, and when it was his time, he was ready. He never wanted to be a burden on anyone. That was not being a responsible servant."

What an honor that Sarah invited me to such a sacred place. Sarah's story was sacred. This time was sacred, and I wondered how long it had been since she'd opened up like this. I saw her struggle. I watched her fidget with the pen, unsure whether to satisfy her organized side by writing something down. I also saw her fight to control her emotions. It was as if she was trying to unlock a door inside her, but she had no key.

"Sounds like your father already made this decision for you," I responded. "It seems like you are being responsible by honoring his wishes."

There it was, a breakthrough! So many things happened at once. Sarah's eyes lit up, and she raised her head. She placed her pen down on the table and, for the first time, seemed completely at peace. It was so simple and right there in front of her the whole time. She didn't need to make any decision. Howard had already made the decision for her. What she needed was a key to unlock a door of acceptance. A door in her life's mansion that apparently had been locked. Once unlocked, the door opened up a room for self-care. This key was permission.

Sarah needed permission to move forward, to make a decision, and to begin caring for herself. She still had a role to play. Sarah needed permission to transition from the role of stoic caregiver to grieving daughter. She needed permission to begin preparing herself to live without her father. But for some reason, she couldn't give herself permission. There was a respected boundary she could not cross. By giving her permission, I put the power of unlocking that door back in her hands. But Sarah was not through. She had one more request.

LAST WORDS

"Would you do me a favor?" Sarah asked. "After you pull the tube, would you promise to pray aloud with my father? I want the last words he may hear to be words of comfort." I melted in gratitude. What a privilege. It was one thing to care for patients during their final moments but to pray aloud with someone felt like another level of honor. Contemplating that my words may be the last words someone hears brought me to a level of humility I never thought possible.

As amazing as this honor was, I realized that, just like my original phone call to my parents, I experienced little to no emotions. Here I was, sharing an intimate moment with a daughter who was about to lose her father, and I felt flat. Where was the guy who performed on stage?

I had no time to analyze the question. Duty called. I suggested Sarah wait outside of Howard's room. I began my ritual. Stillness and silence protected the room. Then the sounds of equipment removal broke through. First, the slight tearing of the Velcro resonated as I removed Howard's tube holder. Second, the sudden rush of air gushed from the leak I created by deflating the airway cuff. Last, the mechanics of the vent announced its goodbye as I turned off the power. At this point, I usually leave, but I had a promise to fulfill.

"Sarah, do you mind coming in the room for a moment?" I asked.

I wanted Sarah to be part of this. I wanted her to watch me lower myself beside her father's ear and see me pray words of comfort and truth because ultimately, I wasn't preparing Howard. I was preparing Sarah. After I prayed, I quietly left the room to give Sarah time alone with her father. I hoped that Sarah could use the time to grieve and explore that room inside her that she may have never explored before.

KEY EXCHANGE

I tried to enjoy the two days off I had after Sarah's event. I tried to relax and rejuvenate, but I failed. Lately, life was busier and more stressed on my days off than when I worked. In addition to working full-time in the hospital, I was taking two graduate courses in seminary. The reading alone took two days to complete! There weren't enough hours in the week to work, study, and write papers, let alone rejuvenate. Vacations with my wife always were planned to occur next month. When next month arrived, nothing changed. I worked, studied, and announced that a vacation would occur the following month. When I returned to work, I knew to expect the usual workload and similar patients. I received exactly what I thought. What I didn't expect was what the nurse said to me as I entered the ICU.

"Jim, we moved the patient you withdrew from the vent to a private room on the other wing," she explained. I couldn't believe it. Howard was still with us! What was Sarah's state? She finally accepted that she was losing her father, but now what was she feeling?

The first chance I had I went to Howard's room. When I opened the door, confusion rushed over me. No lights illuminated except for one lamp that lit the corner of the bed. Someone had lowered the blinds, and the air seemed stale. It was as if the air in the room had been unmoved for days. I looked at Howard. He still breathed, but he was more labored. He looked peaceful, but I knew he was close to the end.

Suddenly the door to the bathroom opened, and I saw Sarah. I almost didn't recognize her. She had bags under her eyes along with a vacant stare. She looked like she was on the verge of tears, but something prevented her. When Sarah saw me, she spoke without any introductions or greetings.

"I haven't slept in over 48 hours," she announced.

"Why not?" I asked.

"Because I wanted to be here for Dad," Sarah answered. "And I didn't know what else to do." That was the first time I heard Sarah refer to Howard as "Dad." Something had changed in Sarah, but yet something hadn't. The room seemed set for grieving, but Sarah couldn't. She had resorted back to her role as the stoic caregiver, but not completely. She seemed conflicted. The previously unlocked door to self-care and healing appeared locked again because of Howard's presence. Sarah needed help. She needed another key.

"Sarah, why don't you go home?" I asked.

"I don't know, what if something happens?" she responded.

"We'll call you if there is any change in your dad's condition," I said. "In the meantime, Sarah, it's okay for you to go home."

And there it was again, something so simple but so elusive. I had given another key of permission to unlock the door to self-care. Sarah knew she needed to go home, to sleep, and to grieve, but she couldn't give herself permission. Permission had to come from someone else. If it did, the burden to care for her father would be lifted, and she wouldn't feel guilty about caring for herself.

"You know, I think I will," Sarah announced, surprising herself. "Thank you, Jim. I needed to hear that."

I was pleased Sarah finally decided to take care of herself. There was nothing more for her to do for her father. I started to leave so Sarah could be alone when Sarah stopped me. "Jim," she said. "If you don't mind my saying so, you look tired too. How was your time off?"

"It was fine," I responded with my proverbial sigh. "But it was very busy."

"Well, maybe *you* should take a break," Sarah said like someone pointing out the obvious.

And there it was, something so simple but yet so elusive. A few words of permission pulled back the curtain to my performance on stage. It suddenly dawned on me what changed during that acting exercise. I hadn't become an incredible actor. Instead, the stage provided the opportunity for me to be emotionally present in my own story because, in the theater, everyone gives you permission to express your feelings. Everyone welcomes vulnerability, even encourages it. Vulnerability is necessary for self-care. But like Sarah, I couldn't give myself permission. Now I could. Sarah and I had exchanged keys!

The healthcare environment breeds locked doors to self-care. However, healthcare workers often lock their own doors. Caregivers have an obligation: the patient's care comes first. Unfortunately, patient care comes at the expense of self-care. There is always another patient and another situation requiring your presence. Thus, caregivers frequently neglect themselves for the sake of their patients. Sarah's key reminded me that quality patient care would suffer if I did not take time to care for myself.

Working in healthcare is challenging and emotionally taxing. I knew I needed time to relax and be vulnerable, but I did not feel I could give myself permission. The one with authority gives the keys of permission. Strangely, Sarah seemed to represent my patients. She had authority, and only she could offer this key to me.

Holding this key felt foreign. I felt empowered! I realized I didn't need to be on stage to have permission to express my emotions. All I needed was a key, a tool that I could use to open the door to self-care anytime I wanted. Sarah provided me that key.

When I returned home, my wife sensed something was different. Before she could question me, I made an announcement.

"Honey, guess what? I asked rhetorically. "It's time. The locked door to the trip to Aruba is now open. Pack your bags!"

"Really?" she asked, surprised and excited. "That's fantastic! But I thought we couldn't take time off right now. What changed? And what door are you talking about?"

114

"It's a long story," I answered. "Let's just say someone gave me the right key."

REEL TO REAL

Sarah's Key is a movie about a young girl's experiences in German-occupied Paris during World War II. When French police attempt to apprehend Sarah's family, Sarah hides her younger brother by locking him in a secret closet. Sarah takes the key and plans to rescue her younger brother at a later time, but she is captured by the police and sent to a concentration camp.

This movie reminds me how important and impactful film can be. Early on in my career, I enjoyed watching and participating in theater. It was a hobby. I knew almost immediately that I did not want to pursue it as a career. It was fun and a release from the daily strains of working in healthcare. Hobbies are great tools to mitigate burnout, provided we make them a priority. Surprisingly, the theater also provided me permission to deal with issues I hadn't dealt with before. A good story moves people to act and affects change. Though it provides entertainment, it also can be a powerful tool of self-care to minimize and prevent burnout.

SMOKE SCREEN TEST

Are you making it a priority to find a hobby? Do you return to work refreshed? When is the last time you took five minutes just for yourself? Take time for yourself to refuel. No one ever said on their death bed, "I wish I had spent more time working."

Finding a hobby and making it a priority can reverse burnout.

CHAPTER 10

KEEPING THE FAITH

"WATCH ME, DADDY!" PETITIONED Ruthy as she proudly jumped one inch higher on the trampoline.

"That's great!" replied Jake, getting a little tired of watching his daughter. Ruthy was a precocious four-year-old with a magnetic personality. Each person Ruthy came near seemed to melt. With her fiery red hair and penetrating blue-green eyes, Ruthy put people at ease. If you were sad, she instinctually comforted you. If you were frustrated, she could calm you down. "It's okay," she would say. "Ruthy can make it better."

Ruthy seemed to love all things: people, animals, and especially play. Though Ruthy often acted older than she was, she enjoyed being a child. Like so many others her age, Ruthy believed the world revolved around her. When she spoke, she thought people should take notes. When she hosted a tea party, everyone should attend. When she performed her compulsory gymnastics routine on the trampoline, she deserved applause, especially from her father.

Ruthy was an only child and the first grandchild. Her parents, Anna and Jake, struggled for years to conceive her. After almost a decade of infertility, they attempted artificial insemination. The first attempt failed, but the second attempt succeeded. Ruthy came into the world at a high financial and spiritual cost. Ruthy's parents had their faith tested. They thought the reason for their infertility had been because they lacked the appropriate amount of faith. The reason for their successful conception, they surmised, was because they finally had enough faith and God rewarded that. But that faith would be tested again. Tragedy would cause Ruthy's parents to rethink their belief.

THE WORLD TURNS UPSIDE DOWN

"That's enough jumping for now," Jake told Ruthy. "It's time to take a break." Ruthy begrudgingly obeyed her father and stepped down from the trampoline. Her eyes showed disappointment. "You are not supposed to stop an Olympic gymnast in the middle of her performance," she said.

"You can finish it later," Jake said. "For now, why don't you invite Ben over to play?" Ruthy's eyes quickly lit up at the suggestion. Ben lived next door and was a couple of years older than Ruthy. "Of course," she said. "We'll have a tea party. Ben loves to have tea with me." Jake knew that Ben did not necessarily enjoy tea, but he did enjoy playing with Ruthy, and Jake needed to focus. It was cooking time.

One weekend a month during the summer many of the families near the neighborhood cul-de-sac gathered at one house and had a picnic. It was a young neighborhood demographic. Each couple was in their late twenties but only Anna and Jake and the next door neighbor had children. Anna and Jake were hosting this month. Unlike the other families, Anna and Jake took hosting seriously. Jake was a wizard at the grill. He cooked burgers, chicken, pizza, and a smattering of other foods to the delight of everyone. This weekend, the menu was ribs and a handful of hotdogs for the picky eater.

Not to be outdone, Anna would display her talents as well. Though she didn't have the cooking prowess of her husband, she did have an incredible creative gift. The word around the neighborhood was that with the right plates and decorations, Anna could make dog manure look appetizing. This year Anna wanted to create an elaborate watermelon display. Everyone looked forward to when Anna and Jake hosted picnic weekend.

Before Ruthy headed over to see Ben, Jake noticed she had swiped a hot dog. *That's my smart little girl*, he thought. *A hot dog would be a better incentive to entice Ben to play with her than tea.* Jake smiled and started to work on the ribs. In addition to his grill, Jake had a top-of-the-line smoker. The ribs had already been smoking for a while, and now it was time to add the sauce.

"The secret is smoking the ribs dry," Jake would say when asked. "The mopping of the ribs with sauce comes last." Jake was proud of his culinary abilities and enjoyed sharing the results with his neighbors. "Thirty minutes to go, folks," Jake announced after lathering up the ribs that already smelled amazing. "I hope you're all hungry!"

The announcement set Anna into motion. Chips, salsa, and veggie trays had been resting on the table since the picnic started. But they were just the opening act to the headlining performance about to happen. Jake motioned to Anna. The unveiling of her watermelon creation was at hand.

Anna entered the house and a dramatic moment later exited the sliding door carrying the most magnificent fruit display anyone had ever seen. "It's a watermelon waterfall!" one neighbor shouted in disbelief. Everyone clapped and cheered in delight. Anna had shaped and cut pieces of watermelon to look like a picturesque mountain scene. There were watermelon evergreen trees, watermelon birds and squirrels, and a working watermelon waterfall equipped with lights and actual running water. Somehow Anna had managed to make watermelon art. Jake smiled as he watched his wife humbly soak up the praise for her work. *She deserves it*, he thought. *She loves creating and entertaining. She is in her element.*

After Anna took a dramatic pause for accolades, she began to walk toward the table to set her artwork down. Suddenly, Ben, the neighbor boy, came running over to Anna. Jake couldn't hear what Ben said. He was too far away at the grill. The next moment Anna's eyes grew as large as saucers, and she dropped her beautiful watermelon platter on the ground. *That stupid kid!* Jake thought. *If he tripped her, even by accident, I'll …* Jake's thoughts were interrupted.

Just as quickly as Anna had dropped her artwork, she screamed, "Ruthy!" Anna began running to the front of the house. Jake realized the situation was serious and quickly followed behind.

Seconds later they both arrived at the front yard. Ruthy lay still. Her once rosy complexion was now blue. She was not moving and she was not breathing. Jake sprang into action. He had taken a CPR course a few years ago just in case of an emergency. Jake blew air into Ruthy's mouth and felt for a pulse. Nothing. He pressed down on her chest.

"I'll call 911!" a neighbor shouted. Anna stood alone in disbelief.

A few minutes later an ambulance arrived. The EMT's took over. At first, they struggled to place an artificial airway into Ruthy's throat while they continued CPR. Moments later they succeeded and rushed Ruthy and Anna to the hospital in the ambulance while Jake followed closely behind.

Ruthy arrived at the emergency room in under ten minutes. Immediately, the staff took over. Monitors erupted in noise. IV's dripped. Orders announced. Organized chaos ruled the room. Hospital personnel escorted Anna and Jake to another waiting area while the medical team performed their duties. Anna and Jake did not speak. They just sat together holding each other's hand.

One agonizing hour passed. Finally, a young physician entered the waiting room and asked to speak with Anna and Jake. "We managed to stabilize Ruthy," he said.

"What does that mean?" Jake asked confused.

"Ruthy's heart stopped beating," the physician replied. "We were able to start it again with the help of the EMT's and your quick reactions. All Ruthy's vital signs are stable, but she is not responding at this moment."

"Can we see her?" Jake asked.

"Of course," the physician responded. "She is still in the ER, but we will transfer her to the Intensive Care Unit momentarily."

Anna and Jake entered the emergency room and pulled back the curtain where Ruthy lay. They stared in shock. Aside from the large tube in her throat and a few monitors, Ruthy looked good.

"She looks like she's sleeping," Anna said, which were the first words she uttered since she saw Ruthy lying in the front yard.

"Tell me as best you can what happened," the physician said.

"Ruthy and Ben, the neighbor's kid, were playing," Jake responded somberly. "I was grilling, and Anna was bringing out her watermelon platter when Ben ran up to Anna. He told her that Ruthy suddenly fell asleep after she started eating a hotdog and wouldn't wake up. My wife screamed, and we ran to the front yard and found Ruthy. That's when we called 911."

"We found a fragment of a hotdog in Ruthy's throat," the physician explained. It was lodged deep in her airway."

"It's out now, right?" Jake asked.

"Yes, we removed it," the physician answered. "The problem is the hotdog occluded Ruthy's airway, preventing any oxygen from getting to her brain. We don't know how long Ruthy went without oxygen. The longer the deprivation, the more damage it causes."

"What do we do now?" Jake asked tearfully.

"We are going to run some tests to determine the severity of the damage," the physician replied. "When we know something, we will let you know."

The news couldn't have been worse. Jake wept.

Just a few hours ago, I told her to stop jumping on the trampoline, Jake thought. *How could this happen? Why wasn't I with her? I was so focused on cooking and hosting. I shouldn't have left her alone.*

Anna did not speak nor cry. She sat and stared at Ruthy.

She looks so peaceful, Anna thought. *If she had her Cinderella pajamas on, I'd swear we were at home putting her down to bed.*

The hospital staff transferred Ruthy to the ICU. The next day, physicians ordered several diagnostic tests. Neurologists assessed her pain reflexes as well as her cranial nerve responses. An electro-encephalogram (EEG) was ordered, and later medical personnel performed an apnea test. The Respiratory Therapist disconnected the ventilator to assess respirations. No noticeable response noted. A blood sample confirmed the assessment. No respirations discovered even at a cellular level. A physician entered the room to discuss the results.

"We ran a full range of diagnostic tests, and I wish I had better news," the physician announced sadly. "The preliminary tests revealed what we had expected. Ruthy is brain dead." Anna and Jake said nothing. "We will wait twenty-four hours and rerun the tests," the physician continued. "However, I don't think the diagnosis will change. I'm sorry for this sad news." Anna and Jake sat numbly clinging to each other's hand as if they were lifelines to the other's sanity.

The next day Ruthy remained unchanged. Staff repeated the tests. Identical results came back. The same physician who ran the tests the day before entered the room to break the news. He saw Anna and Jake in practically the same location as the day before. *I doubt they went home last night,* he thought. *I hate this part of my job.*

"Unfortunately," the physician began, "the second round of tests revealed the same thing. Ruthy is brain dead. At this point, there is nothing else we can do. Our next step is to remove the tube from Ruthy's throat and turn off the machine. Again, my deepest sympathies for your loss."

"No," Anna announced almost inaudibly.

"Pardon?" the physician responded.

"No," Anna said more emphatically. "You're not taking my child off the machine. She is not dead!"

"I'm sorry, I don't understand," replied the physician.

"Doc," interrupted Jake, "could you give us a moment?"

"Of course," said the physician. "I'll step outside for a moment." *They're in shock*, he thought. *"It's understandable, but they can't refuse the removal of the ventilator to what is, in essence, a corpse ... can they?*

The physician walked out of the room and closed the door. Separating the door and the wall was a six-inch wide pane of glass allowing an outsider's view into the room. The physician saw Anna and Jake discussing the situation. Though he could not hear the conversation, he could tell they were not arguing. Several minutes later the door opened. Jake appeared. He motioned to the physician to enter the room again.

"After further discussion, we have decided to leave the tube and ventilator in place," Jake stated. "We want to do everything we can for our daughter. What are our treatment options?"

"I understand how difficult this situation is," the physician said, "but there seems to be a misunderstanding. There are no other options. Ruthy has expired."

"We don't accept that," Jake stated as Anna sat holding Ruthy's hand, oblivious to the conversation. "We just need more faith. We will wait and see."

"With all due respect," the physician responded, "you can't refuse a diagnosis of death. Besides, what are you waiting on?"

"We are waiting for a miracle," Jake stated confidently as he sat down beside his wife.

GOD'S TIMING

Over the next two days, Ruthy's case became known. Staff members discussed the case, and everyone's heart ached for Anna and Jake. Ruthy had a way of drawing people in. The staff wanted to offer condolences but because of the parents' viewpoint, they decided it would be best to give them their space. The following morning a tall, gray-haired man entered Ruthy's room and introduced himself. "I am Chaplain Finn," he said respectfully in a deep baritone voice. "I understand you wanted to see me."

"Yes," Jake said. "We asked for a chaplain because we wanted prayer for our daughter. We need help with our faith and are waiting for a miracle."

"It would be an honor and a privilege to pray for you," Finn responded. "But before I do, may I ask you some questions?"

"Certainly," Jake responded.

"What faith do you follow?" Finn asked.

"Christian," Jake responded. "We go to a local church when we can, but we haven't been in a while."

"I understand," Finn replied. "May I ask, what do you mean when you say you need help with your faith and you're waiting for a miracle."

"We're waiting for God to heal our daughter," Jake replied. "But he hasn't because, evidently, we don't have enough faith yet."

"And how long will you have to wait?" Finn asked.

"We don't know," replied Jake. "That's one of the reasons we called you. We thought maybe because you're a chaplain you might be able to increase our trust in God. Then God will heal our daughter."

"I see," replied Finn. "So, you think your daughter's lack of healing is correlated to your lack of faith?" Finn asked.

"Yes," Jake replied. "Jesus once told a sick woman that it was her faith that healed her."

"I remember," Finn said. "That was mentioned in the Gospels. But do you remember the story of Shadrach, Meshach, and Abednego?" asked Finn.

"Yes," replied Jake. "That was in the Old Testament. They were thrown in the furnace but survived."

126

"Indeed," replied Finn. "They had tremendous faith in God. What I find interesting is they mention that God will rescue them from certain death, but if He does not, they will still trust in Him. They implied that their faith did not guarantee rescue."

"That's interesting," said Jake.

"Do you think the apostle Paul lacked faith in God?" asked Finn.

"Of course not," Jake replied emphatically.

"How about Jesus?" Finn asked.

"That's obvious," Jake answered. "No one ever had more faith than Him."

"I agree," replied Finn. "But you see, they both suffered. Paul suffered from some kind of pain throughout his life, and Jesus was not spared an agonizing death. So, if neither Paul nor Jesus lacked faith but they both suffered, then it stands to reason that their healing did not necessarily correlate with their faith."

"I never looked at it like that," Jake replied. "Does that mean we shouldn't pray for Ruthy?"

"Of course not," Finn answered. "That's the beauty of being in a relationship with God. You can ask Him for anything! But let me ask you another question. Hypothetically, if Ruthy passed away, where would she be right now?"

"She'd be in heaven," Jake answered.

"If you were Ruthy, would you want to come back?" asked Finn.

"No," Jake answered, lowering his head and realizing the impact of his response.

"Then when you say you're waiting and praying for a miracle, for whom are you really praying?" asked Finn.

"It's for me!" Anna responded loudly, startling Jake.

Anna had been silent throughout the whole conversation. For a moment, Jake forgot she was in the room. Anna had barely spoken a word since the accident. Her sole concern was for Ruthy. Or so she thought.

Anna let go of Ruthy's hand, stood up, and turned to Finn. "We're praying this for me! I can't imagine life without my daughter. We struggled so long to have her, and after four short years, I can't bear to think she's gone. The thought of living without her terrifies me. Everything I did, I did for her. I suppose now she's the one person all of this is not for."

"What are you saying?" asked a stunned Jake.

"I'm saying, I guess there's no need for prayer after all," replied Anna.

"Quite the contrary," Finn said. "Let us pray for Ruthy and both of you. Let us pray for that miracle. God certainly can heal, but that doesn't mean He will."

Finn leaned over and placed one hand on Ruthy's leg and one on Anna's shoulder. He closed his eyes and prayed the most angelic prayer Anna and Jake ever heard. He prayed for that miracle, but more importantly, he prayed for comfort for Anna and Jake. Finn prayed for peace and assurance. He prayed for God's presence to be felt and for Anna and Jake to be surrounded by the right people to walk alongside them during this difficult time.

After the prayer, Anna and Jake hugged Finn and thanked him. Finn left the room quietly, allowing Anna and Jake another moment with their daughter. They held hands and stared at her. There was no change in her condition. After several minutes of silence Anna said, "It's time." Without asking for clarification, Jake knew what she meant.

"I'll see if the physician's available," Jake said as he turned to leave. Just before he reached the door, another knock sounded, and the door opened a crack. A middle-aged woman entered and introduced herself.

"Hello, my name is Mrs. Riley," she said softly. "I'm the chaplain here. I understand you wanted to see me."

"Oh, thank you, Mrs. Riley," Jake replied. "We just spoke with the other chaplain. There's no need. I think we're okay now."

"The other chaplain?" Mrs. Riley questioned.

"Yes, Chaplain Finn," Jake replied. "He was extremely helpful."

"Excuse me, but there's no Chaplain Finn on staff," Mrs. Riley said. "I'm the only chaplain at this hospital." Anna and Jake looked at each other while the hair on both of their necks stood up.

No, they both thought. *It couldn't be.* Anna and Jake looked at each other for several seconds until Anna spoke.

"It *was* a very angelic prayer," she said, considering the possibilities. "And Ruthy does attract all kinds of people," Anna said, wondering if "people" was the right word choice in this situation.

"Are you sure there is nothing I can do for you?" asked Mrs. Riley, interrupting Anna and Jake's awkward staring.

"Well," Anna answered. "What do you know about angels?"

REEL TO REAL

Arguably, the most important part of one's life is one's worldview. Everyone has one. The lens by which we view reality affects everything we do and is how we answer life's big questions. In the movie *Keeping the Faith*, two young men have their worldview tested when their beautiful childhood friend reenters their lives. One develops a relationship with the girl, but the relationship quickly runs into turmoil due to his Jewish beliefs.

Like the movie, the decisions Anna and Jake needed to make were greatly affected by their worldview. They believed that the amount of faith they had corresponded to God's action. In a sense, they believed the power to heal fell on the strength of their faith and not the object of that faith.

But just because they believed it, didn't make it true. Truth is what corresponds to reality. For Anna and Jake, their belief or worldview didn't correspond to reality empirically or experientially. When they realized that, they adjusted their belief. Truth didn't change, but their understanding of it did.

Burnout occurs when demand exceeds resources. An accurate

worldview can be the difference between burnout and fulfillment. There is an overwhelming peace and joy that comes with being convinced that your worldview is accurate. Some of my favorite moments have been sitting around a table discussing various personal beliefs with a group of friends. Inevitably, you discover what you know and what you don't. The challenging questions force you to dig deeper and uncover gaps in your worldview. When the gaps are filled, satisfaction ensues. And being satisfied prevents burning out.

Of all the tools I've learned in my twenty plus years of healthcare, security in my faith has been the most important. Deeply understanding my worldview has protected me from burning out again more than any other tool. Know what you know and why you know it. When people ask why I follow Christianity, my answer is simple: because I'm convinced it's true. This should be everyone's response, though some balk at the notion.

Faith or worldview is a personal belief akin to an opinion, some say. However, everyone demands truth from their doctors and from their bank. What makes religion or faith any different? The point is to follow the evidence and never stop growing in your faith. Be humble enough to accept when you may be wrong. If you do, that humility could lead to a better understanding of truth making burnout an area of little concern.

SMOKE SCREEN TEST

What is your worldview? Why do you hold it? What evidence do you have to show its validity? If you can't answer these questions, then you are not familiar enough with your worldview. Take time to assess your beliefs. It will help quell burnout and provide answers to life beyond the present. What is more important than that?

Everyone has a particular faith or worldview. Knowing what you believe and why you believe it affects your identity and behavior and could be the most important tool to manage burnout.

EPILOGUE

When demands exceed resources, people burn out. Lethargy, frustration, and depression appear in its wake. Thankfully, the simple tools mentioned in this book can lessen the toll burnout can have on your career. Some of these tools may work for you, others may not. Each person is unique. Find which ones work for you and commit to implementing them in your practice. Your health and the health of your patients depend on it.

These stories are also a reminder of the importance of sharing. The twenty-first century marks an age of connections but few relationships. With a few clicks on a computer or phone, you can be connected to thousands of people. But these are not relationships. Sharing is communicating the essence of who you are, what you think, and what you feel. Sharing is about being authentic, not revealing your deepest, darkest secrets. But many people do not feel comfortable sharing. In that case, writing down your thoughts, talking with a counselor or coach, or even forming your ideas into narratives that provide tools to help manage burnout can be a substitute. Taking preventative actions can clarify your perspective or position, be therapeutic, and refresh your attitude. Claim your tools, whatever they may be, and incorporate them into your life to promote greater well-being. Caregivers need care too.

APPENDIX

Summary of Burnout Tools

Chapter 1: ANGER MANAGEMENT—**Laughing** provides physiological benefits to mitigate stress.

Chapter 2: WEEKEND AT BERNIE'S—Finding your **niche** in your workplace can decrease stress.

Chapter 3: THE BUCKET LIST—**Remembering** why you chose your field can help you focus your attention on the important things.

Chapter 4: BURNT—Sometimes **evaluating** your situation is necessary to ensure you're in the right field.

Chapter 5: THERE'S SOMETHING ABOUT MARY—Developing proper **habits** decreases stress and compounds into self-improvement.

Chapter 6: FLATLINERS—Taking a moment to diaphragmatically **breathe** can alleviate the damage of stress to your body.

Chapter 7: FLATLINERS—REVISITED—Taking **time** to rest, relax, and separate yourself from stress quells burnout.

Chapter 8: REAR WINDOW—**Asking** for help is important to decrease burnout and assist in life's direction.

Chapter 9: SARAH'S KEY—Finding a **hobby** and making it a priority can reverse burnout.

Chapter 10: KEEPING THE FAITH—Everyone has a particular **faith** or worldview. Knowing what you believe and why you believe it affects your identity, behavior, and could be the most important tool to manage burnout.

What Readers Are Saying

In today's medical care environment, burnout is an increasingly discussed concern. Damron takes us along on his journey to the consequences of the often unrecognized stresses of caring for others. Part of any solution is to recognize the problem. Damron's stories and transparency will hit a note in many of us. If you're noticing increasing fatigue, loss of job satisfaction, and the anemic recovery with time off, you might be experiencing the smokescreen of burn out. An enjoyable and, at times, humorous ride.

~William J. Bicket, MD, Ethics Committee Chair, Atrium Health

Health care professionals struggle with stress and even burnout all too often. In his new book, *Smoke Screening: Narratives to Navigate Caregiver Burnout*, Jim Damron offers health care professionals a soothing anodyne in the face of workplace struggles. Organized around the titles of popular movies, Damron offers the reader a number of clinical narratives that conclude with a variety of pearls. Accessibly written and often laced with trenchant humor, Damron does a great service for the clinicians caring for patients. As he concludes in his book: "Caregivers need care too."

~Kayhan Parsi, JD, PhD, Professor and Graduate Program Director, Neiswanger Institute for Bioethics, Loyola University Chicago Stritch School of Medicine

Jim does not disappoint with this easy, must-read for any caregiver in need of practical ways to manage burnout. Jim's perspective is spot-on and will have you ready to immediately give one (or all) of his burnout tools a try!

~ Natasha Tyson, MHA, SSBB, RRT, AVP Clinical Services, Atrium Health

Being a health care professional is hard in many ways, and it requires a great deal of balance to keep from falling from the high wire. Jim Damron teaches us to find our place in our profession to help us from drowning in the stress of patient care. Jim's stories are meaningful lessons and a delightful read.

~Kenneth Haas, DC, CCSP, Founder Haas Wellness Center

If you want practical tips for managing burnout, delivered in a humorous, engaging, and heartfelt manner, this is your book. Jim weaves personal experiences with useful nuggets to address and alleviate burnout. I found myself laughing, crying, and relating to each story.

*~Carol K. Woodard MSN, RN, CCRN-K,
Critical Care New Graduate Nurse Residency Program Coordinator*

Made in the USA
Middletown, DE
26 August 2022

72325481R00086